Living and Loving with Parkinson's Disease

Our Partnership Through a 45-Year Journey

Rolf Lulloff, MD

M&B Global Solutions Inc.
Green Bay, Wisconsin (USA)

Living and Loving with Parkinson's Disease
Our Partnership Through a 45-Year Journey

Front cover image: Rolf and Annie Lulloff enjoy time in 2010 at their happy place, Sanibel Island, Florida.

Back cover image: Rolf and Annie Lulloff during a vacation on Saint Martin in March 1988.

ISBN: 978-1-942731-46-7

Printed by Seaway Printing Company Inc.
Designed and published by M&B Global Solutions Inc.

Green Bay, Wisconsin (USA)

Dedication

To the memory of Annie,
her resilience, and ongoing legacy.

This is for all the people who will benefit
from what we learned during her journey.

Contents

Preface

Few life events are more emotionally trying than watching your spouse endure a decades-long health challenge. It is a journey that requires immense patience and perseverance for everyone involved, and in the case of my wife Annie and me, unconditional love.

Ann Lulloff passed away in my arms at home on February 12, 2021, after a battle with Parkinson's disease that we can trace back more than four decades. Annie's early symptoms did not affect her motor skills. This important aspect of her early onset of Parkinson's did not lend itself to an accurate diagnosis of this degenerative neurological disorder, even for a physician like me. I specialized in orthopedic surgery during my medical career and likely was more equipped than most people to recognize symptoms and understand what was going on.

Yet despite my best efforts and those of Annie's physicians, we couldn't understand what was causing her decline. Finally, after thirteen years of knowing something wasn't right with her health, two of the classic motor symptoms of Parkinson's disease – slowness of movement and tremors – began to appear. When Annie finally slept away at eighty and a half years old, she had provided a remarkable example of resilience over the course of the thirty-one years since her diagnosis and more than forty-four years since our journey with Parkinson's began.

My goal in sharing our story is to pass on what we learned, offer suggestions for medical professionals, care partners and care persons alike, and provide hope for those who may be facing a similar journey. Above all, I want to highlight the important role that love and the support of family and friends played in making our journey one of joy and teamwork rather than simply survival.

You will notice that I use the terms "care partner" and "care person" throughout this book rather than "caregivers" and "patients." Annie and I were care partners for each other in different ways. I first came across the more appropriate "care partner" terminology in literature from the Davis Phinney Foundation for Parkinson's, and I have been using it ever since.

Many people over the years witnessed Annie and me together and saw how we did things. They tell me I was so wonderful to her, but she was more wonderful to me. She taught me so much and we learned how to deal with things as a team. Things that gradually became more challenging as her condition deteriorated. Things we didn't foresee coming into play.

Annie was the force driving the process throughout our journey. On the occasions when we would encounter a new challenge, we would find a way to change what we were doing and adapt. Sometimes we would try things that did not end up being helpful even though they may have been accepted treatments by the medical community. She often taught me by example how to identify what the actual problem was and what steps we needed to take in order to turn things around. We learned how to deal with those challenges in ways that contributed to our quality of life. Many of those ways were new to us, and indeed not acknowledged as the standard of care.

So many people told me, "Rolf, you've got to write a book about Ann's journey. You have learned so much and this is pertinent information. Doctors don't understand what it's like to live with this disease. You guys lived with it, and you discovered many tricks of the trade."

I finally decided they are right. Annie and I have a duty to share what we learned through our journey so others can benefit. This is not just a book for care partners. It is also for care persons who are early in their journey. The person with Parkinson's disease is in control of the situation, although they may be overwhelmed at times. You are in the battle together. This is Annie's story, and Annie drove the process of our journey.

Annie and me at our house in Green Bay, Wisconsin, in 2011. She had been diagnosed with Parkinson's disease for more than twenty years by this point and had symptoms going back at least thirty-five years.

It may seem as though you are constantly chasing a moving target – and oftentimes you are – but in many cases others have gone down this road before and can offer advice. Let me assure you the tips and information I share in this book are not advanced medicine. They are simple, easy-to-follow suggestions that virtually anyone can understand.

I have included useful information that everyone who is a direct care partner or extended family member can use in navigating the obstacle courses ahead. This information will help you and your care person maximize your quality of life. In the early stages of such a journey, the care person will be able to comprehend and actively participate in following appropriate strategies. Annie certainly did.

Closer to home, this book is for all the people who knew Annie, understood who she was, and saw how she dealt with life's challenges. Telling our story certainly is therapeutic for me as well. But more importantly, Annie's story is pertinent for care partners and care persons who are dealing with significant health problems, especially neurodegenerative diseases such as Parkinson's and the various dementias. Neurodegenerative diseases develop when brain cells and their connections progressively lose function over time.

Keep in mind as you read our story that just because certain strategies worked for Annie and me, they may not work for you, and vice versa. I am not your doctor. You need to have accurate information that is pertinent to your case as you face evolving challenges in your journey and new symptoms make their appearances. Consult your doctor to get help interpreting that information so you can make the right decisions. Your commitment to gathering information and advocating for yourself or your loved one is critical in making the best of a challenging situation.

"You guys are lucky because you're a doctor and you're in love," people would tell us.

While that was true, we still had to find ways to adapt when things were going badly. Annie was exceptionally smart, she was an athlete, she was married to a physician who worked a lot, and above all, she was a fighter. She was tougher than nails.

Love and gratitude are so important when dealing with health challenges. We found that if you live with love and gratitude, you'll be okay. I told Annie on the day of her diagnosis that we would fight this disease and make a difference. This book is my way of continuing Annie's fighting spirit so we can, in fact, make a difference in the lives of so many people with the lessons we learned during our journey.

Annie and I are very proud to make this contribution.

Chapter 1

Our Story

As with any story, it helps to know something about the main characters, and in this case it is Annie and me. We took very different routes to our eventual connection at the University of Wisconsin-Madison, some of which I did not know until corresponding with a few of her friends during the writing of this book.

Annie grew up as Ann Keller in La Crosse, Wisconsin, the oldest of three children born to Albert and Zita Keller. Her Nebraska-born father was a self-employed construction manager who was a real straight shooter. Her mother, Zita McDonough, was several years older than her husband. She was very artistic, even performing as a ballerina in New York City early in her life. Another daughter, Kathy, whom we call "Sis," came along about fifteen months after Annie, followed by her brother, Albert Jr. "Buzz," a few years later.

Interestingly, the Keller family has a significant history of Parkinson's disease. Annie's mother and brother both died as a result of Parkinson's. While we cannot say that most cases of Parkinson's disease are hereditary, the prevalence of the affliction in this family shows there likely is a strong connection.

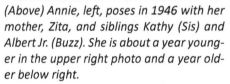

(Above) Annie, left, poses in 1946 with her mother, Zita, and siblings Kathy (Sis) and Albert Jr. (Buzz). She is about a year younger in the upper right photo and a year older below right.

After completing elementary school, Annie attended Campus School at Wisconsin State College, La Crosse (now UW-La Crosse) for grades seven through nine. It was a lab teaching facility for the college's students who were interested in education, and Annie loved it there. She and her classmates then moved on to La Crosse Central High School for their final three years, graduating in 1958. She maintained relationships with that group for many years. Annie was a very good tennis player in high school and took lessons in the summer. She and her friends traveled to many tournaments throughout the region. On a couple of those summers, Annie went with friends and a tennis coach to Rochester, Minnesota, where they stayed with host families while participating in tournaments. Annie was very impressed with staying on Pill Hill, the historic neighborhood that is home to many of the Mayo

Clinic medical staff.

Annie really liked science, leading her to pursue college education as a medical technologist. She attended UW-La Crosse for one year before transferring to UW-Madison. However, studying hard and keeping her nose clean wasn't always high on the priority list for her there.

Char "Shindy" McLaughlin was Annie's roommate during Annie's junior year in 1962-63. Shindy recalls first meeting her in Cole Hall, a women's residence dorm, at the beginning of second semester in 1962. According to Shindy, Annie had been put on strict probation because of her propensity to break dorm rules. The powers that be assigned her to a single room right next to the resident assistant (RA) so they could keep a closer eye on her.

"Ann and I had an immediate rapport," Shindy says. "She was so different from me that it is amazing she even cared to hang around with me. I was so straight-laced! She pulled me out of my tight little shell and I learned to enjoy Madison life."

Annie failed organic chemistry during her probationary period in the dorms. She retook the course the following semester and squeaked by with a D to earn the credits, but her grade point average felt the effects and dropped below 2.0.

The new friends and three other girls rented an apartment the following fall on Lathrop Street, only a block from Camp Randall Stadium. That was the first of many rules the quintet broke, as the apartments allowed a maximum of four. Girls who had lived in Cole Hall occupied all three floors.

"We had the best time living there," Shindy says. "We had some of the best parties in our apartment, and Ann organized most of them. Ann was the taskmaster in our apartment. She put together a calendar of jobs for the week for each of us. There was cooking, cleaning, and grocery shopping."

As one would expect, there was plenty of drama to go around with five college girls living under the same roof. The first girl to leave did so because of a relationship with a guy for whom the girl's parents did not approve. Soon afterward, a second roommate left after she graduated and received a good job offer in Chicago. The landlord was another source of stress. Annie was convinced he was a peeping Tom and even reported him to the police at one point.

"We had constant run-ins with him regarding the heat in our apartment," Shindy recalls. "Ann and I reported him to the student housing authority. They came to inspect and found several violations, which he was cited for. I think he literally hated us by the time we moved out in May."

Annie graduated from UW-Madison in 1963 with her bachelor's degree in medical technology securely in hand.

My small town roots

Annie and I were about a year and a half apart in age and one hundred miles in distance growing up. My upbringing was such that I knew I was going to be a doctor by the time I was in first grade. My parents, Harold and Jane Lulloff, owned Lulloff Furniture Store and Funeral Home in the southwestern Wisconsin town of Dodgeville (pop. 2,911 in 1960), and we lived upstairs. My dad's father, Adolph Lulloff, had purchased the businesses (furniture was a common business pairing for funeral homes) in 1918 and operated them until his death in 1949. My parents were the first husband/wife licensed funeral directors in the state of Wisconsin. I was in the funeral home all the time and was used to being around death, so I never had any fear of any aspect of medicine or working with bodies. It was just part of our upbringing.

We had great sports teams at Dodgeville High School during this period, and I participated in football, basketball, and track for the Dodgers. It was common for kids to participate in multiple sports at that time, and it still is when it comes to small schools like Dodgeville. Most of us also participated in music, FFA (Future Farmers of America), and other clubs. There were all of sixty-two kids in the graduating class of 1960.

We didn't win a single football game during my sophomore year, but things turned around immediately when the administration hired Charlie Thompson to coach the team prior to my junior season. Charlie was about six-foot-four and 260 pounds, and had been a star player at Ripon College in central Wisconsin. He was our Spanish teacher and quickly became one of my favorites. We hit it off well, and I swear we talked more about football than Spanish during class. I was not the natural athlete that my older brother Kim was, but I had a brain and Coach Thompson needed someone who could call the plays. I was the starting quarterback my junior and senior seasons, and we tied for the conference championship that next season with our archrival, Darlington.

Kim was eight years older than me and a superb athlete. In fact, he is a member of the Dodgeville High School Hall of Fame. Kim had his sights on becoming a professional golfer and tried out for the team at the University of Wisconsin. He won a playoff to supposedly make

The Lulloff family on the occasion of my brother Kim's graduation from medical school in 1960. My mother, Jane, is on the left, then me, my father, Harold, and Kim. It also happened to be the spring I graduated from Dodgeville (Wis.) High School.

the Badgers' squad, but instead they gave the final spot to a guy whose parents were significant donors to the university. Kim was so fed up with the politics that he shifted his energies toward medical school and eventually earned his degree from Marquette University. Like me after him, Kim went on to enjoy a successful career as an orthopedic surgeon.

A love connection in the lab

Annie's degree qualified her to work in labs doing blood testing and other types of tests. She would evaluate the blood, perform the appropriate tests, and submit a report to the physician of record. She did on-the-job training for three months and was looking for a part-time job in the summer of 1963 when our paths crossed.

I had just completed my third year of pre-med studies and had been accepted into medical school to begin that fall. I had a government-sponsored job doing research in which I tested shrews to see if they were hypermetabolic. In other words, I was learning how to measure the metabolic energy levels in these animals, which in humans can be an indicator of cancer or other issues. I would get up in the middle of the night, wade through swamps, empty the traps, bring back the shrews to the lab, and inject them with drugs to measure their metabolism. Annie's part-time job happened to involve cleaning that lab.

So there I am, working with shrews, and in walks this cute, hopefully eligible college grad. She would walk in at four o'clock every day to clean the lab. Turns out she had a steady boyfriend, which was not the news I wanted to hear.

Shindy told me recently that Annie had called early that summer to tell her about me.

"There's a new guy in our lab," Shindy says Annie told her. "I like his looks. He's going to medical school. I think I'm going to have to break up with my boyfriend."

Likewise, one of Annie's friends from her middle school years at Campus School in La Crosse tells me that Annie also called her during this period to talk about the new medical student in the lab where she worked.

"I think he's worth pursuing," she recalls Annie saying.

I had no clue about this part of the story. I thought I had to pursue Annie, and instead it turns out she had her sights set on me! Two additional friends, both of whom did not know Shindy, have told me Annie confided in them about her interest in me as well.

On Thursday, July 25, 1963, the other medical student who was doing research in the lab asked if I was dating anybody.

"You should ask Ann out," he urged.

"She's got a boyfriend," I replied.

"No, they broke up last week," he countered.

My outlook changed in an instant. All I could think about the rest of the day was asking her for a date. At four o'clock that day, Annie showed up for work. She was wearing Bermuda shorts and a blouse that was untucked. She looked wonderful in anything she wore.

"Would you like to have a couple of beers tonight?" I asked, hoping the casual invitation would hit the right tone.

She must not have been in a good mood because she gave me this angry, almost threatening look. I imagined her thinking, "Who told him that I broke up with my boyfriend and gave away my privacy?"

Thankfully, her demeanor changed almost immediately. She got a smile on her face and said, "I'd like that."

After work, I walked the two blocks from the hospital to her apartment, and together we walked down to The Pub, a college beer bar on State Street. Young people at that time could not drink hard liquor until age twenty-one. College students like me, however, could drink beer legally at age eighteen. Beer bars were popular hangouts at a notorious party school like UW-Madison. We sat in a booth on the left wall and talked nonstop for about three hours over three Heileman's Special Export beers apiece. We really hit it off.

I walked her back home at the end of the night, and at the door she looked at me and asked, "Might I expect to be able to see you again?"

"I'd like that," I answered.

"So would I," she said.

Without hesitation, we embraced and kissed. All I could think about as I walked on air the five blocks back to my fraternity house was how neat she was, and that I was going to marry this wonderful woman. I had dated a girl in high school and she dumped me. I didn't really date anyone for a while after that. No one seemed to fit until Annie walked into that lab.

The bad news was Annie was going to be moving to Milwaukee at the end of summer because she had accepted a job in a hospital there. I asked myself, "Am I going to let her get away from me?" The answer, of course, was no.

We saw each other as much as we could for two months until she moved, and then every other weekend after that. Usually I would drive over to Milwaukee, but one weekend per month she would take the Badger Bus to Madison and stay with one of her friends. We dreaded the feeling of separation every time one of us had to return home.

Annie was fun-loving, and she brought her personality into me. I needed that to get through the stress of my life at that time. I was dependent on my parents to pay for my education, even though they wanted to do it. They felt obligated to do for me what they had done for Kim. He already had his MD. I loved my big brother and he was always very nice to me. (Kim had a successful medical career before passing away as a result of Alzheimer's disease in September 2021, seven months after Annie's passing.)

Annie and I were greatly attracted to each other and fell in love quickly. Did that mean we were definitely going to get married? I wasn't thinking that way initially, but it wasn't long before I convinced myself this long-distance relationship stuff was insane. I needed the stability

The happiest day of our lives. July 18, 1964.

that her friendship meant to me. She was the right lady for me, and now we would find out if I was the right man for her. I was as sure as I could be; now it was my job to make sure she bought into it. I could tell by her responsiveness that she was attracted to me. Therefore, why fight it?

I drove to Milwaukee on January 18, 1964, for our regular bi-weekly visit with plans to pop the question. I hadn't really thought through how to phrase my proposal; I just knew I was going to ask this girl to marry me. It wasn't the most graceful proposal in history.

"Let's get married," I blurted out.

"What?!" Annie responded, obviously shocked by my statement.

"Let's get married," I repeated.

"Are you sure?"

I could sense that her brain was racing, asking herself questions such as, "Does Rolf really understand what he's asking?" and "Am I willing to take this risk?" She knew I was going to be in medical school for a while.

"Yes," I said, confident in my feelings.

"Then I accept," she answered with a smile.

We hugged and kissed, and a little later that evening went out for a nice dinner at Frenchy's Restaurant on Milwaukee's north side. We were excited about the future and the way we wanted it to go. Of course, we did not think about life's challenges that may lie ahead in that moment.

When we dropped the bombshell that we were engaged on my parents soon afterward, they were shocked and very dubious of our decision, especially my mother. They were paying my tuition, but they immediately asked if I thought about who was going to support me.

"Yes, Ann has a good job and we're going to live very conservatively," I answered.

I desired the stability of a solid relationship and didn't want to be worried about dating during a time in which I would have to immerse myself in studies. I knew Annie was the right person for me anyway, so why wait?

Annie moved back to Madison two months later at the end of March 1964, leaving the hospital administration in Milwaukee not at all happy to be losing her. She was a good worker, a nice person, and people loved her. I'm sure that was stressful for her. She shared a two-bedroom apartment in Madison with someone she did not know previously and went back to work at University Hospitals in Madison in the same lab where she had interned. We got married a few months later on July 18, 1964, one week short of one year since the day I asked her out for our first date.

Annie loved planning the wedding with help from some of her friends, and I let her take charge of it all. I was plenty busy with my studies and did only as instructed. Our ceremony was in La Crosse at the First Presbyterian Church. The regular minister was on leave, so we had a substitute for our service. We met him once and again at the rehearsal dinner. It was hotter than blazes that day, and we got married at noon. There was no air conditioning in the church.

After we pushed through the discomfort of the heat and humidity for several rounds of pictures, it was off to the Cerise dinner club for a brief reception. We had an open bar, hors d'oeuvres, and wedding cake. We left about 4 p.m. for a short honeymoon, planning to drive across Wisconsin the first day, and then north to a resort near the Upper Michigan border. We had reservations at the Holiday Inn in Neenah the first night, and of course we were on a limited budget. We arrived to find our room rate was $21, almost double the $12.50 they had quoted me over the phone.

"When I made the reservation, I was told the rate was $12.50," I said to the desk clerk.

"That rate is only for honeymooners," she replied.

"This is our wedding night!" I exclaimed.

"Well, you were supposed to tell us that."

"I did!"

We got the $12.50 rate.

We went for a swim in the hotel pool the next morning before driving forty-five minutes north to Green Bay, where we had reservations that evening at the Downtowner Motel. It also had a pool, since we wanted to have access to a pool anyplace we stayed on this trip.

We were on our way to the motel and driving down Webster Avenue, which at that time was a two-lane road, when who do I see coming the opposite direction but Fred Lamont. Fred was a classmate of mine in medical school and a Green Bay native. Annie had met him previously at our fraternity house in Madison, and we had even invited him to our wedding. We honked at each other, stopped in the middle of the road, opened our windows to talk, and Fred suggested we pull into the nearby Lorelei Inn to have a beer. What are the chances of that happening?

We continued our trip the next day with a short drive up to Door County, Wisconsin's summer vacation area in the thumb of the state. We had never been to Door County, and we figured we could then catch a ferry up there from Sturgeon Bay, across the bay of Green Bay to Marinette, and then up to King's Gateway resort north of Eagle River for four nights and three days. Unfortunately, no such ferry existed, so we had to drive all the way back down to Green Bay to get around the bay and head north.

It turned out to be a really long drive, and part way there we pulled into a filling station in the small town of Mountain so Annie could use the restroom. Only there was no restroom. The attendant directed Annie to an outhouse in back of the station. Annie was a trooper and had to go, so out to the outhouse she went.

She got back into the car and we continued our drive. It wasn't long before both of us wondered aloud what smelled so badly. Turns out the outhouse had been in a pasture (this was Wisconsin, after all), and Annie had stepped in cow manure with her nice shoes. There was no way to adequately clean them, so I told her she had to throw them away. Annie tossed the shoes out the window and we stopped in Eagle River

Annie and me, along with her parents, Zita and Albert Keller, at my graduation from medical school at the University of Wisconsin-Madison, 1967.

later on to buy a new pair. It was another unexpected expense for these newlyweds.

Our real honeymoon came the following January on a ski trip to Colorado. We were going to drive both ways to save money, leaving Madison on the Friday of semester break for ten days. Jim Blotz, a friend of mine from Dodgeville and one of the groomsmen in our wedding, asked if he could come along and help with the driving. I had a Chevrolet Monza Spyder, which was a very sporty car, but not very big. We had skis on the back and three people and luggage jammed inside. It was an unseasonably warm forty-five degrees and raining when we left Madison.

The highway was flooded by the time we got as far as East Dubuque, Illinois, and the temperature was dropping. As we drove downhill about 11 p.m. into Council Bluffs, Iowa, Jim hit the brakes and we began to skid. He suggested it would be best if I drive with the roads being slick, and I agreed. The problem was, we couldn't tell if there was ice on the road or not. I got out to check and almost fell on my butt. Black ice, which for those of you not familiar with winter driving, is virtually impossible to see and extremely slippery. It is one of the most dangerous road conditions there is.

We decided to seek refuge in a little motel, sharing a room with a pair of double beds. We woke up the next morning to see eight to ten inches of snow on top of the ice sheet that used to be a highway. The motel owner told us to wait a while, and that a plow would be coming through soon that we could follow. It would lead us forty miles to the west, and by that time we would find the interstate open.

We followed his advice and continued westward, finally reaching Loveland Pass west of Denver that night. They had just opened the pass, which sits at 11,990 feet, two hours earlier. We pulled into Aspen at five in the morning, took a nap, and were on the hills by noon. We had rented a miner's cabin that included a bedroom for Annie and me, and an upstairs loft for Jim.

We were not good skiers at all. I took Annie on one of the intermediate hills, which was still tough for skiers of our ability. We got halfway down and she said, "I hate you! You had no business bringing me up here!"

Our marriage survived that episode and many much more challenging than that. She was my "Annie" and I was her "Rolfie."

Coming back to Wisconsin, we hit another storm and had to sit at the bottom of Loveland Pass waiting for it to open. We had a couple of beers that morning and were playing Euchre (a card game), when all of a sudden word came that we could go. We were the first car in line to get over that pass, and once up there we saw an oil tanker that had jack-knifed. Annie said she had to pee, so we pulled over and had her go behind the car.

"Annie, you've got the world record today for peeing at the highest altitude," I said.

It was a belated honeymoon, but it was memorable!

In working on this book, I was able to relive our love affair and realize how amazing it was. How natural it was. My advice is to keep your eyes open and count your blessings as you appreciate all that is good in your life journey.

Medical school and babies

Our first year of marriage coincided with my second year of medical school at UW-Madison. We didn't have much money because I was studying hard, so Annie worked as many hours as she could. She worked full-time as a medical technologist and we both moonlighted in hospital labs to make some extra money.

Our first apartment together was two blocks from Camp Randall Stadium, upstairs from a shoe store on Grant Street. The only room that had water was the bathroom, which had a tub but no shower. There was a split pipe that ran up to the ceiling, across the bedroom, and into what had been a closet. That little room had a window, and it was our "kitchen." We had a little stove and a drain so we could wash dishes in there. Rent was $50 per month and there was no lease. The building owners were upset with us when we left six months later to move into married student housing in the Eagle Heights neighborhood. Our new rent was $100 per month, but at least we now had a shower in the bathroom.

I was working in the same lab as the previous summer when we had met. I'm sure we had become fodder for lab gossip while we were dating, but it wasn't bad because the people there loved Ann. She was outgoing, honest, and reliable.

Annie knew I had to study a lot and my hours were not always conducive to her meal planning. She was a good cook, which was helpful for me. One day, I walked into the apartment and asked, "What stinks?"

She gave me a dirty look as if to say, "What did you just say?"

"Something smells," I repeated, completely oblivious to the doghouse looming in my immediate future.

"That's your dinner," Annie stated sternly.

I remember it was some sort of rice dish and I didn't like it. However, I learned to never say anything like that again. She was so angry, but at least she didn't divorce me on the spot.

Annie liked to play tennis and joined the Nielsen Tennis Club on campus. I had started to use running as a mental release from the pressures I was feeling. Running was growing in popularity around Madison at that time, and there were nice trails to run on in Eagle Heights. I had run track in high school, but going out for a long run alone is a very different experience. I enjoy the meditation aspect of running as well as the physical activity, and it continues to be part of my fitness regime to this day. I found I felt better, studied better, and frankly, was a much better husband to Annie when I was running regularly. It was beneficial in that I wouldn't have any pent-up stress to take out on her or the kids. Annie took care of our social calendar, which often included a few other couples with whom we would do things.

I had a preceptorship rotation with a clinic in Janesville, Wiscon-

The Lulloff family in 1971 included Annie, Susan, Sarah, Rolf, and Andy in front.

sin, for three months during my senior year of medical school. I knew I wanted to specialize in orthopedics by this point, so my preceptorship featured spending four weeks with two general surgeons, four weeks with the orthopedic surgeons, and then four weeks with the main preceptor internist.

Annie took a leave of absence from University Hospitals so she could work at the lab in Janesville. We lived in an upstairs room of a rooming house and got our meals at the hospital. We shared a bathroom with a guy we never saw once. We knew he was there, though, because we could hear the toilet flush. Annie and I played some tennis and golfed together that summer at the local municipal course.

Annie was about six months pregnant with our first child while in Janesville, and Susan was born that fall, a little more than two years into our marriage, on October 26, 1966. Like most new parents, we struggled to adjust our lives to the arrival of this bundle of joy. It seemed she would get an ear infection every time we brought her to daycare.

Medical school is by far not the end of your education when you are on the road to becoming a physician. There are internships and residency commitments to fulfill, and in the spring of 1967 we had a decision to make about where I would serve my year of internship. I had an opportunity in Salt Lake City with University of Utah Affiliated Hospitals, and together we decided this would be a good choice. We moved there in June 1967, shortly after I graduated from medical school. We had sixty straight days of temperatures 90 degrees or above that summer. But we bit the bullet and toughed it out.

Part of our decision to go to Utah came down to the fact we also wanted to experience ski country for a year. When I was in medical school, we drove up to Indianhead Mountain in the Upper Peninsula of Michigan for a weekend ski trip with three other medical school students and their girlfriends. We were the only married couple, so we got three connected rooms at a little hotel in Bessemer, Michigan. Annie and I stayed in the middle room and acted as the chaperones. The three guys stayed in one room and the three girls in the other ... or so we thought!

Frank Weinhold, who later became a radiologist in Green Bay, was there with his fiancée, Judy. They got married the next summer while Annie was pregnant with Susan. Annie served as the designated driver at the wedding, which had an open bar. She was the glue that held multiple groups together on a social level. Everybody loved her and she loved them back. That dynamic would continue throughout our journey. We always had great support from our friends.

One great thing about living in Salt Lake City is the hospital encouraged us to go skiing when I had a half day off. We would get a babysitter for Susan and go up to the Alta Ski Area. There was a big snowfall in November of that year and I had the day off. It was about a forty-five minute drive up to Alta. We got off the lift at the top and soon sank into powder up to our waist. There was no one up there other than us, and no way to get down other than to ski. So we started going down the mountain. We would fall down and laugh, and get up and try again. We didn't get hurt because of the soft powder, but it sure was a tiring trek down.

It soon became apparent, however, that we were fish out of water in this Mormon city. My pay was $300 per month and our rent was $220 per month. We had decided that Annie would be a full-time mother during my internship, since I would not be home much at all.

"Annie," I said, "we'll borrow the money we need and get by this year, then we'll go back to Wisconsin."

"Thank you," she replied.

As it turned out, I was away from home more often than we had anticipated. I was supposed to be on call no more than every third night the first month of my internship. But by the second month, it was every other night. Sometimes I would work all night long on call at the hospital and then work my regular day shift until four or five o'clock in the afternoon. Occasionally, I would get to spend two nights in a row at home.

Finding some level of work-life balance was very important to me. I knew I'd be working hard, but I also had a wife and daughter. It was asking a lot to have Annie put up with things during that one tough year. I was very disappointed about my workload, so I went to the department chief with whom I had interviewed.

"We've had people back out and we're short on staff, so everybody has to pick up the slack," the chief told me.

On the bright side, this was a great medical center and the people were good. I worked my butt off and learned a lot. It was good, practical experience, which is what I wanted to get. On top of it all, I had to prepare to take my medical boards so I could earn my license to practice medicine. I took those tests in June 1968 at the end of my internship.

Early on during my internship year, our next major decision involved where I would serve my four years of orthopedic surgery residency. I had been accepted into the residency program back in Madison, but I also had been accepted in Salt Lake City. The Salt Lake City program accepted only two new residents per year, which meant I would be working hard all the time. The chief of the orthopedic department was a highly respected, nationally known head of pediatric orthopedic surgery at Salt Lake City Shrine Hospital. He was high-powered in every way and a gentleman, so I was torn. Do I want to go through four years of high-powered orthopedic residency here in Utah and be away from family?

That weekend, Annie and I talked about it. She said, "I won't divorce you if you stay here in Salt Lake City, but I would be happier in Madison."

"So would I," I replied.

The skiing might be better in Utah, but our family and social circles were back in Wisconsin. So we moved back to Madison at the end of June 1968 and I started my residency promptly on July 1, 1968. By this time, Annie was pregnant with our second daughter, Sarah, who joined us three weeks early on December 28, 1968.

Annie loved being pregnant and taking care of babies. She was absolutely enamored with being a mother. The summer after Sarah was born, we took a long weekend getaway and Annie ended up getting pregnant again. Immediately, however, she could feel something wasn't right.

"I might be pregnant, but I don't feel pregnant," she said.

We went to see her doctor and he confirmed the pregnancy. She called me at work about a month later to report she was spotting badly and the doctor wanted her to come in right away. I drove home and brought her in, and twenty minutes later he came out to tell me the baby was lost.

"It was not a good pregnancy," he said. "It was not meant to be. Hug your wife a lot, because she's going to need it."

Annie and I cried a lot that day. It was one of the most emotionally powerful times of our lives together, and we bonded even more as a result.

Enjoying life in Madison

We had a good life in Madison despite all the hours I was working. Annie was able to play tennis at the university's Nielsen Tennis Stadium for a small fee because I was considered faculty. She used to play with Eric and Beth Heiden's mother, Nancy, who was a very accomplished player. Eric would later win five gold medals and Beth a bronze medal in speed skating at the 1980 Winter Olympics. Nancy's husband, Jack, was a long-time orthopedic surgeon in Madison.

I went to Canada at one point on a fishing trip with my dad and brother for a week. Was Annie happy about that? No, she wasn't. I only went to Canada that one time while we were married, because I knew how tough that was on her. She was making daily sacrifices as I pursued my medical career.

That wasn't the only occasion in which Annie had to fly solo when it came to caring for our children. I was going into my last year of orthopedic residency in the summer of 1971 when an opportunity arose to join Dr. Henry Okagaki, the chief of pediatric orthopedics at UW Hospitals, on a two-week trip to Hong Kong. There was a world-renowned orthopedic spine surgeon there whom he knew well, and Henry was already well-respected in Wisconsin for his work performing spinal surgeries on kids with deformities.

Henry was a Japanese American who had lived through internment during World War II. He later joined the US Army Reserves, rose to the rank of general, and was in charge of the University Hospitals Reserve Program. He was a giving sort of person who loved kids, but never had any of his own. He and I hit it off really well.

"We'll go learn some new spine techniques he's doing," Henry said. "I need a resident along to have someone capable of doing the operations with me."

Annie reluctantly agreed with my desire to go to Hong Kong, mainly because Henry really liked her and he took special pictures of our children. If she had not liked Henry so much, she likely would not have gone along with this idea. Regardless of her blessing, I felt guilty as heck when I left. Annie was very worried about my travels, thinking in terms of a worst case scenario in which our plane would crash. Looking back, it may have been an early sign of the extreme anxiety we would later learn can be associated with Parkinson's disease.

Our son Andrew had just been born May 13, 1971, so Annie had three kids age four and younger to watch while I went off to Hong Kong. I missed our wedding anniversary because of that trip. I felt so guilty about it, and I brought back all sorts of presents for her. Years later, Henry and I shared at least three patients that he had taken care of in Madison and I cared for after we moved to Green Bay.

I tried to never leave Annie again. She was, without a doubt, the most important person in my life, and I realized I had a responsibility to keep her happy.

Our relationship with the University of Wisconsin was huge for us. We both graduated from Madison and enjoyed so many good friendships that began there. We are always proud to have been Badgers. In fact, we sang the alma mater song, *Varsity,* at Annie's celebration of life, and they certainly will at mine as well.

Turmoil, near and far

Annie always displayed a higher level of determination than the average person, and her resilience showed through from the moment we became a couple. Going through those years was challenging on multiple levels, but she always looked at every situation as an opportunity rather than a problem. She ran the household and took care of our children. She ran everything having to do with our family. I was busy working sixty to seventy hours per week, usually eating breakfast with the family only on weekends. Annie told the kids as they got old enough that they had to make their own breakfasts.

At one point during my residency, one of the pediatricians wanted to take his wife on vacation. He asked us if there was any chance we would agree to move into their house with our three kids so we could watch their three kids. We agreed, and all of a sudden Annie had six kids to care for. I earned enough money during my residency and moonlighting three nights per month in the emergency room to make ends meet.

The 1960s were a stressful decade to live through, from the constant threat of nuclear attacks during the Cold War to the Vietnam War and social strife that accompanied that topic. Looking back, it would make sense that some of these major events in history had an effect on Annie's anxiety issues.

The first traumatic event came on November 22, 1963, with the assassination of President John Kennedy. I was walking back from the anatomy lab about noon after spending the morning dissecting a cadaver when a few guys came out of the house telling me what had happened. It was a Friday, and Annie and I were planning to join my dad and his longstanding work partner at the Green Bay Packers' game in Milwaukee against the Cleveland Browns on Sunday. (The Packers played a couple of home games per season in Milwaukee until 1994.) The National Football League decided to play the weekend's games, a decision which elicited understandable criticism. Talk about a somber game. The Packers won, but there was very little cheering from the subdued crowd.

Some events were less impactful, but created stress in the moment nonetheless. One that comes to mind was my graduation from medical school on June 6, 1967. We were about to move to Salt Lake City for my internship program – which was stressful in itself – when the Six-Day War broke out in the Middle East between Israel and the Arab states of Egypt, Jordan, and Syria. The scheduled guest speaker at commencement was U Thant, the secretary-general of the United Nations. He had to cancel his appearance to deal with the war.

The following year, 1968, has been described as one of the worst in US history. Tops on the list were the assassinations of Martin Luther King Jr. and Sen. Robert Kennedy, riots at the Democratic National Convention in Chicago, civil rights conflicts, and demonstrations across the country protesting America's role in the Vietnam War. The husband of one of Annie's high school classmates was killed in Vietnam during our time in Salt Lake City.

The atmosphere in Madison was tense when we returned in June 1968 from Salt Lake City. Many students were protesting the Vietnam War, and the level of conflict was becoming more intense. By the spring of 1970, the dominant emotion was hate, hate, hate. The campus was in turmoil. Annie and I were somewhat separated from what was going on, but we could not completely get away from it.

News that the United States had conducted carpet-bombing operations in Cambodia in late April was the catalyst to a general student strike on May 1, 1970. Wisconsin's Veterans Against the War in Vietnam led a march to the Capitol, which stands at the opposite end of State Street from the UW campus. Demonstrators faced off against the National Guard to battle for control of the campus. I was at the hospital, which was under lockdown because the battle likely would take place right behind our building. We were told it was going to be bad.

Then something happened. It rained so hard for an hour – right as the conflict was about to start – that nobody could do anything. Demonstrators were pounding on the doors of the hospital to get inside, but we didn't let anyone in. God had put the fire out.

Things were ramping up again the next night, although the crowd wasn't quite as large. Again, God doused the fire with another rainstorm. By this point, protesters who had come from outside the Madison area began to disperse. Annie's brother was involved in the protests, which I'm sure affected her.

Similar demonstrations were taking place on college campuses across the country, including Kent State University in Ohio. Members of the Ohio National Guard fired into a crowd of demonstrators there on May 4, killing four young people and wounding nine others. Chaos erupted, and a national student strike caused many colleges and universities to temporarily close.

The UW campus avoided the worst of the protests until later that summer. At 3:42 a.m. on August 24, 1970, four men using homemade explosives set off a massive blast outside Sterling Hall. They were targeting the Army Math Research Center located there. The explosion killed one researcher, a thirty-three-year-old father of three named Robert Fassnacht, and injured four others. It also damaged twenty-six buildings. I was on call that night and had to go in to treat one of the injured.

A military detour

We knew I would owe Uncle Sam two years of military service at some point, which helped with planning greatly. There was still a draft at this time and we knew I would have to complete a service commitment, so after completing my residency, it was time for me to go into the US Army. First up was three weeks of basic training in July 1972 at Fort Sam Houston in San Antonio, Texas. We were moving out of our duplex in Madison at the time and it didn't make sense to move the family down there for that short of a period. Plus, Annie had to get the apartment ready for the movers. The army paid for that, but she still had to make sure everything was taken care of.

I saw a guy carrying a tennis racquet when I arrived at basic training in San Antonio. I struck up a conversation and we ended up rooming together in the hotel where they put us up. The Vietnam War was beginning to de-escalate at this point and the chances of me being shipped overseas had decreased dramatically. I have no doubt that the situation would have been very different had I come out from residency a year earlier.

It was like another honeymoon when I flew back to

Annie holding Andy with Susan (left) and Sarah (front) in La Crosse, Wisconsin, spring of 1972.

Madison after completing basic training. We were so happy to see each other that we were like newlyweds. We drove to Dodgeville and stayed overnight with my parents. There were a number of aunts and uncles there partying us up, and at a certain point that night they said, "Time for you two to go to bed." So off to bed we went!

The army moved us to Fort Dix, New Jersey, on August 1, 1972. I went right to the hospital to report for duty as Annie and the kids sat in the car. I met the NCO (non-commissioned officer) in charge of the clinic, a man named Sgt. Roosevelt Murray. He cut quite an imposing figure at about six-foot-four, 260 pounds. I had my uniform on with the designation of my rank as a major.

"Welcome, we've been expecting you," he said. "We're excited to have you. I'm sort of in charge here, but you (the doctors) are the bosses medically. We're here for you. Have you met Col. Edward Anthony Rankin yet?"

"No, I haven't," I replied. "You are the first person I've met."

"He's a great chief," Sgt. Murray continued. "He's in his office on second floor. Go upstairs and meet him."

I had spoken with Col. Rankin on the phone previously, but had never met him. He was a big guy as well, about six-foot-three and 190 pounds with a great build. I saluted upon entering his office, and he was quick to disperse with the formalities.

"It's Tony," he said with a smile.

"It's Rolf," I replied, immediately feeling more at ease.

"Do you have quarters yet?" he asked.

"No, sir. It will be about a week until we do."

He asked where we planned to stay, and I told him we had reserved a room at the Doughboy Inn on post. This was a huge military community, with Naval Air Engineering Station Lakehurst and McGuire Air Force Base right next door. The facilities today are known as Joint Base McGuire-Dix-Lakehurst. The property at the time featured a twelve-story hospital and a huge retirement community.

"Rolf," Col. Rankin said, "my wife and I and our two boys are going on leave tomorrow for a week. Our quarters are perfectly clean. You can stay in our place."

He went to hand me a key, but I knew that Annie would not be comfortable with that and politely declined his offer. Tony and I ended up becoming best of friends. He was there for my first year and then retired from the army. He became president of the American Academy of Orthopaedic Surgeons about fifteen years later. He's still a close friend and a true gentleman.

We had five fully trained orthopedic surgeons on staff and five general medical officers assigned full-time to orthopedics. Because this was a basic training center, the orthopedics department supplied the sick call coverage for a significant number of the basic trainees, and our general medical officers handled those duties.

Annie and I had a great two years at Fort Dix, and we maintained close friendships with four couples who were there at the same time. She played a lot of tennis and really enjoyed our time there. Our three kids would play on a blanket in the corner of the court while Annie kept an eye on them in between points. Annie was an extravert and formed good friendships with the women and the couples. We both liked being with people and doing things together.

I never remember Annie complaining. Talk about an amazing, resilient lady! I was always struck by that, and I still am.

Becoming "The Running Doctor"

My interest in running took a jump shortly after we moved to Fort Dix, and Annie was very supportive. I came back from a run on Sunday, September 10, 1972, in time to watch the end of the marathon from the Olympics taking place in Munich, Germany. The world was captivated by the tragic events taking place during the Games, especially since less than a week earlier, members of the Palestinian terrorist group Black September had killed two members of the Israeli Olympic team and took the rest hostage. The remaining nine members of the team died in a failed rescue attempt by the West German police.

Upon turning on the TV, I saw that American star Frank Shorter was in the lead of the marathon! No American had won the Olympic marathon since 1908, and this was very exciting. Frank would go on to win, but not before an imposter entered the stadium a minute in front of him, robbing Frank of the hero's welcome he so deserved. It was another strange moment in the most unusual Olympics ever held.

I thought, "If Frank can win the Olympic Marathon, I should be able to at least finish one. Maybe I should try to run the Boston Marathon."

Little did I know, but I would become part of the running boom that took the United States by storm as a result of Frank's victory. Prior to that, running for fun was not something many people did.

Of course, completing a 26.2-mile marathon is easier said than done. It requires hours of training, building up your endurance to the point where you can withstand the rigors of three to four hours of intense exercise. Marathon training is as much about the mental aspect as the physical, and Annie gave me the green light to chase this goal.

You can't just show up in Boston to run in the annual April event. You have to record a qualifying time based on your age and sex. In my case, I needed to run a marathon faster than three hours, thirty minutes in order to qualify for the Boston Marathon. I set the 1974 race as my target, giving me about a year and a half to train while I was in the army.

There were plenty of ups and downs during that time as I pushed myself to attain this goal. Annie was very supportive and never made me feel guilty for the time it took. It seemed I was always hungry at night because of all the calories I was burning through. I would bring a bowl of popcorn to bed to share, and that was the only part of the process that drew my wife's ire.

"You can't keep doing that," she said. "I'm gaining weight, but you're not!"

I did qualify for Boston, posting a time of 3 hours, 29 minutes in March of 1974, only about a month before the Boston Marathon. On Easter Sunday, we drove up to Boston after sunrise services to prepare for the next day's race. We drove the course route when we arrived, and about halfway through Annie asked, "Aren't we at the finish line yet?" Twenty-six miles takes a long time traveling at city speeds, especially with three little kids in the car with you. This may have been the first time she truly understood the challenge I was facing.

We had a motel room booked in Hopkinton, which is where the point-to-point race begins. The next morning, we drove with our kids to the starting area in advance of the noon race start. I went into the nearby post office to ask permission to park there.

"Are you running in the race?" the clerk asked.

"Yes, I am."

"Then sure, that's fine."

I showed Annie where to meet me after the race on a map and headed for the starting line. It was a chilly day, as is typical for the third Monday of April in the Northeast. I felt great and could tell I was running faster than I did in my qualifying race just a month earlier. I finished in 3:09:46, twenty minutes faster than my qualifying race, which is a lot. I was elated!

I found Annie and the kids near the finish line, and we agreed to meet back there in a little while so I could recover and she could get some food with the kids. When she came back forty-five minutes later, she reached into her pocket and exclaimed, "Oh my God! I don't have my billfold. I must have been pick-pocketed!"

Her billfold carried cash, our credit cards, her driver's license, everything. We were crushed. Two weeks later, her billfold arrived in the mail. There was no cash in it, but remarkably, everything else was there.

Although Annie was very supportive of my running, I promised her after that Boston race that I would not do another marathon. However, I did run Boston again four years later; this time in 2:51, or about 6:32 per mile. This performance would stand as my lifetime best. I ended up finishing about a dozen marathons during my running career, including four Boston Marathons and the New York City Marathon in 1979.

Annie really enjoyed watching the runners finish in New York as she waited for me that year. As long as we were in New York, we decided to try and see the New York Philharmonic. We didn't have tickets and took a chance on standing in line. Unfortunately, everyone in front of us got in and we did not. Oh well, we had a great adventure together anyway.

Setting down roots

It came time for me to take my orthopedic surgery board exams while we were at Fort Dix, and by the summer of 1973, I was working and studying every waking moment. The first time you are eligible to take these boards is after you have been out of residency for at least a year. I was studying and working hard, and making every effort to maintain some semblance of a life with Annie. She was an amazing spouse.

I was accepted to take my boards in September 1973. I flew to Chicago, where they administered the tests, while Annie held down the fort, so to speak, at Fort Dix. The orthopedic surgery boards include a lot of written questions along with three oral exams in front of veteran surgeons from big-name hospital programs. I was walking outside the Palmer House, a big hotel in Chicago, the night before my boards when I stepped on a pile of dog poop. I thought, "Is this an omen?"

I vividly remember one examiner during an oral test was guiding me down a pathway of questions that was setting me up to give a wrong answer, and I realized it. He was doing this on purpose to see how well I knew my stuff. We reached a fork in the road in the procedural decision process of the examination, and I was ready to give him the correct answer. The examiner smiled when I answered correctly and said, "Best of luck to you. You'll be a good orthopedic surgeon."

I understandably felt stressed out after the tests, not helped by the fact I would not learn the results for another month. I flew back to the East Coast and could feel a cold coming on. I was exhausted. My plane landed in Newark about midnight, and it was raining and cold. I stood under a plastic awning, waiting for a bus to come by and take me back to Fort Dix. But the bus didn't show.

"Where's the bus?" I asked an airport employee.

"Sometimes they show, sometimes they don't," he replied.

I stood there until about four in the morning when a bus finally arrived. I was so relieved when I got home. I was even more relieved when I found out I had passed my boards a few weeks later.

My military commitment was coming to an end in 1974 and we knew we wanted to get back to the Midwest. But where? We made two grand tours of several possible landing spots between Illinois, Minnesota, and Wisconsin in October 1973. We didn't have the results from my boards at this point, but we knew we would come back to the Midwest regardless, even if I had to retake the tests.

One of the first places I looked into was the Dean Clinic in Madison. They had four orthopedic surgeons on staff at this multispecialty clinic and I knew those guys. The issue with joining this clinic was there would be competition against the academic center where I trained (UW-Madison) in some ways. Plus, I didn't think I would be as busy as I wanted to be. I had a feeling I would be the low man on the totem pole before I would get an opportunity to do any of the advanced procedures I was interested in doing. Long term, there was no doubt that turning down their offer was the right choice for me. Plus, they wanted me to take care of spinal surgeries, and that was not my area of expertise.

My brother was practicing in Neenah, Wisconsin, but I didn't necessarily think it would be a good idea for me to join him. Kim agreed. In fact, there was no one place that jumped out at us on our first tour through the Midwest. We were pretty much set on taking an offer from a group in DeKalb, Illinois, a little west of Chicago, but we wanted to check out a couple of more options first.

A group in St. Cloud, Minnesota, was very appealing on our second tour of the region. Three of the guys there were nice, but the fourth guy was not. He was not open-minded, and I knew that wouldn't work. He wanted me to do back surgeries, too.

I also interviewed with a group located on the east side of Green Bay. Kim had gone to medical school with one of the physicians and recommended I talk to him. The offices for this group were located close to the two hospitals on the east side of town (Bellin and St. Vincent), and they also covered the lone hospital on the west side, St. Mary's. They had interviewed another candidate previously, and they were candid in telling me they hoped the other candidate would accept their offer. Annie and I had this group listed as a question mark.

After returning to Fort Dix, I received a call from a physician at West Side Clinic in Green Bay. As the name implies, this clinic was on the opposite side of town from the east side group. Green Bay was very much an east side-west side city at the time (and still is to some extent), with the Fox River dividing the city into halves. Some long-time residents seldom – if ever – set foot on the other side of that river.

West Side Clinic had general surgeons on staff, but no one specializing in orthopedic surgery. This physician had seen my name on a list of doctors looking to practice in the region, and he happened to have been a year ahead of me at UW-Madison. I told him that I didn't want to come to Green Bay if I would create turmoil between the competing groups. However, if the east side group's first choice accepted their offer, then I would be open to joining them.

As it turned out, the east side group got their man, and it happened

Our first Christmas in Green Bay, 1974. From left, Andy, Rolf, Sarah, Annie, and Susan.

the same day I spoke with my acquaintance at West Side Clinic. My contact with the east side group called to inform me of their decision, and our conversation featured a pleasant twist I didn't see coming.

"Take a serious look at West Side Clinic," he urged me. "Our practice is on the east side, so it would be great if you could cover St. Mary's from the West Side Clinic. We would welcome you to Green Bay."

In the end, I liked the situation in Green Bay the best of any of the cities we had visited, many of which would have been acceptable. Our decision came down to the fact we felt welcomed by the medical community, and especially the people at West Side Clinic.

I knew I would be busy there; the question was whether I would have any coverage available to back me up when I needed it. I was able to get Dr. Al Freedman to agree to a coverage arrangement, and with that, Annie and I moved our family to Green Bay, Wisconsin. We left Fort Dix on June 22, 1974, and moved into a house we had found in the east-side suburb of Allouez. My contracted starting date at West Side Clinic was July 1. I asked for a week to get settled first as we moved in on July 4, and I actually started at the clinic on July 8, 1974.

Six weeks after we moved to Green Bay, we got a jolt upon learning Annie's father had died of a heart attack.

I worked a lot that first year. I had regular full-time responsibilities, and was on call six nights per week. Dr. Freedman covered for me the other night so Annie and I could go out to dinner. On Christmas Eve, Annie had a terrible cold and was so sick she could barely get off the couch. I was on call, and after finishing my regular workday, I let the answering service know I was at home. I hoped it would be a quiet night so I could stay home with Annie and the kids. Ten minutes later, the phone rang. Dammit.

"We just got a call from Dr. Freedman," said a woman at the answering service. "He said we should tell you he's going to take your call tonight and all day tomorrow until the morning of the twenty-sixth. And he wishes you a Merry Christmas."

Dr. Freedman was Jewish, and he knew Christmas was very important to us. He was such a wonderful, class guy.

Annie got the family settled right away and just took charge when we arrived in Green Bay. She met new friends and started playing tennis at a local club. The medical community was wonderful, and we received invitations to a number of social functions within a month of our arrival. One of them was a party for all the new doctors in town hosted by Dr. John Mills and his wife. It didn't matter which clinic you were with; the event was designed to help those of us new to town meet people. That collegial attitude changed twenty-five years later when larger healthcare systems became entrenched in our community and the medical business turned much more competitive.

People asked me how I got to know so many people in Green Bay. It was because Annie built great relationships. She immediately became our social contact and met all the gals in our neighborhood. We lived next door to the president of West Side Clinic, Dr. Lee Richardson, and his family those first couple of years. He and I always hit it off fine professionally.

I may have been earning our monetary income, but Annie had three or four jobs of her own. She took care of the house, paid many of the bills, shuttled our kids when necessary, did the shopping and food preparation, and ran our social life.

Annie and I had planted roots, and our lives were on the right track.

Chapter 2

First Signs of Trouble

Our lives progressed wonderfully in the first several years after moving to Green Bay. Annie made many friends for herself as well as for us as a couple. We joined Oneida Country Club across town, where many fellow physicians and their families were members. It was a social hub as well as providing a top-notch golf course, outdoor tennis facilities, and even riding stables. We also played tennis at the two racquet clubs in town, Four Seasons and then Western Racquet Club when that opened. Annie loved playing tennis and became one of the best female tennis players in the area. In fact, she was inducted into the Brown County Tennis Hall of Fame on October 26, 1988.

Annie knew lots of people, and therefore, I got to know them, too. In many cases, I got to know the men because Annie got to know their wives first. I used to say, "Ann knows everybody and I'm along for the ride."

We played most of our tennis at Four Seasons, and Annie was at the center of a humorous situation in about 1976 or 1977. We were relatively new in town, and a few people were enjoying a drink after playing.

Annie looked great the evening she was inducted into the Brown County Tennis Hall of Fame on October 26, 1988.

The conversation turned to Bobby Riggs and Billie Jean King, who had played their famous "Battle of the Sexes" match in 1973. Riggs was fifty-five years old and Billie Jean was twenty-nine, and their match came four months after Riggs easily beat another top female pro, Margaret Court. Billie Jean dominated Bobby in three straight sets in a match viewed by an estimated ninety million people worldwide.

"I could beat all the women here," Chuck Bielke, one of the many characters who played at Four Seasons, said in Bobby Riggs fashion.

"You couldn't beat Ann," replied Annie's friend, Sue Hollenbeck.

"I bet I can," Chuck said, doubling down on his boast.

"No, you can't," said his wife, Jewel (who rooted for Annie).

Many club members came to watch the match, and Annie beat him. I was very proud of her.

Annie developed a number of contacts from tennis. It seemed she got to know everybody and everybody knew Annie. I was the type of person who would try to figure out ways to break the ice with people I met, while Annie could bridge any gap without being nosy. She made people feel comfortable.

She was living an active life, in great shape, and seemingly as healthy as could be. There was nothing to foreshadow the coming health challenges that would send our lives into a gradual, but dramatic turn.

When I think back on this time, however, I recognize Annie had dealt with significant emotional turmoil and a variety of stressful situations for many years. She was the wage earner for the first few years of our marriage as I finished up medical school. Plus, she did most of the cooking and cleaning. I can count eleven times that she moved, either as a single woman or with me. I helped carry boxes, but she was the person in charge every time.

Living in Utah was stressful in that we were away from family and friends, we had a baby, and lived on a shoestring budget. Once we returned to Madison, we rented half of a duplex for four years that my parents had purchased. I moonlighted in the emergency room one weekend day and two weeknights per month. Along with my stipend as an orthopedic resident, I made enough money to cover our expenses and a little bit more. It was common for me to doze off at the dinner table the evening after my night shift, since I had to be back at the hospital for 7 a.m. rounds and was running on fumes by evening.

Then it was off to fulfill my military commitment and all that entailed, with the added responsibility of now having three children. We got free housing there and I made a good salary, which helped from a financial perspective. I also moonlighted three nights per month in an emergency room, which gave us a little icing on our financial cake. It is very possible the cumulative effects all of these moves and life changes could have played a role in her Parkinson's onset, but that is pure speculation.

We finally enjoyed some stability once we moved to Green Bay. Annie's job was to be the mom of three kids and run the household. As long as I was making enough money, I told her to go ahead with any house renovations she had in mind. Contractors would come through – some for several projects – and they loved Ann. I had no idea how much some of these projects cost until years later. But hey, you can't take it with you.

Annie's first physical symptoms did not involve involuntary shaking or any of the other motor indicators typically associated with Parkinson's disease. In fact, when her first symptom came at the age of thirty-six – the loss of her sense of smell – we didn't know what to make of it. Today, most people would be more likely to attribute loss of smell to COVID than Parkinson's disease.

"It's gone!" Annie told me that fateful day in 1976. "I can't smell anything, and my sense of taste is not very good, either."

My initial response was to assume those symptoms would improve, but they did not.

"Don't be a jerk, Rolf," I told myself. "This is real. Let's get it checked out."

I took her to see an ear, nose, throat (ENT) specialist, and he could not identify anything that would cause these types of symptoms. He was convinced, however, that it had to be neurologic in nature. We then saw a neurologist, who observed some small calcifications on Annie's CT scan. He also couldn't attribute those to her smell and taste issues, but did agree with the ENT that something neurologic was presenting itself. Non-motor symptoms like these were not considered to fall within the Parkinson's spectrum at the time, but it is mainstream thought today.

Our brains have specialized areas that deal with the various senses. The eyes, nose, taste buds, and ears all send electrical signals to the brain. Our brain takes that input and interprets what to do with the information. Annie's loss of smell was the first sign that Lewy bodies were beginning to attack her brain, although it would be many years before we would understand that. Lewy bodies are a buildup of abnormal proteins that interfere with the normal activity and function of neurons in the brain. (We'll talk more about Lewy bodies in the next chapter.)

I tried to minimize the seriousness of her symptoms in her presence while still acknowledging them. I knew her loss of smell was neurologic in nature, but I didn't realize it was a precursor for something else.

Before long, Annie began to exhibit increased episodes of anxiety and depression. She would have panic attacks, needing to cling to a hallway wall in a mall, and became afraid of doing things as simple as entering a building. We would learn later that psychological issues like these are common aspects of a Parkinson's journey, and in fact can appear long before other symptoms. It is easy for family members to ignore or downplay these symptoms. I recognized them, but was somewhat oblivious to how serious of a problem they were becoming.

I found out much later that this was not the first time Annie had displayed severe anxiety. Her college friend, Shindy, recalls a particular incident when they were living in the apartment on Lathrop Street in Madison in 1962-63 that may have been an indication of the health issues ahead. Annie was very concerned about the results of a titer test she ran on herself while working in the lab. This is a test that measures the presence and amount of antibodies in the blood.

"She said the test showed very high levels, and she had angst over this for quite a while," Shindy explained. "I realize now that a high count could indicate a possible autoimmune disease. I often wondered if this had been an early warning sign of the potential health problems that Ann had."

Annie's incredible resiliency shown through long before her physical symptoms became evident. She admitted to Shindy later that psychological issues were causing her concern.

"One outstanding characteristic of Ann's that came through loud and clear was the resiliency she had to adversity in her life," Shindy told me. "She was visiting the Chicago area for one of your medical conferences and we met for dinner. She talked about her anxiety attacks and how difficult this condition was on her. She resolved that she'd get an answer as to why she had this affliction, and how she would deal with it and move on."

In retrospect, I wonder if a right shoulder issue that first cropped up the day after Susan was born in 1966 might have been an early indicator of future physical problems for Annie. She mentioned her shoulder "feels funny," and I could see that her right scapula (shoulder blade) was winged out a little bit. We took her to see a neurologist at University Hospitals in Madison, where we lived at the time, and he noted she had a neuropathy on the muscles that controlled her scapula, causing them to work improperly and resulting in the abnormal position.

The neurologist made a big issue about potential exposure to toxins, but she hadn't been exposed as far as we knew. I couldn't help but think of this episode after she lost her sense of smell ten years later. The shoulder was the only neurological symptom I could identify until then. I can't say it had anything to do with Parkinson's disease, but I was always struck by the fact this neurologist didn't think it was the result of her sleeping on it wrong or anything like that.

It didn't help Annie's mood in the aftermath of losing her sense of smell that her mother, Zita Keller, was in failing health and beginning to demonstrate symptoms of Parkinson's. Not long after, Annie's sister moved Zita into a long-term nursing facility in her home area of Minneapolis/St. Paul.

When I mentioned that her mother may have Parkinson's disease,

Something cracked up Annie in this Christmas 1987 family photo. (From left) Rolf, Annie, Sarah, Andy, and Susan.

Annie's response was, "I probably have it, too."

I thought to myself that Parkinson's was a distinct possibility, but of course I didn't want to believe it. Could this really be early Parkinson's disease for my Annie? It was a frightening thought. Looking back, I didn't really know what I was looking at. Plus, some of the symptoms developed so gradually that my brain didn't fully realize what was happening. Some brain disorders are not Parkinson's, although they may be related to it. I tried to make sure Annie didn't worry herself to death while being understanding and truthful as needed.

She began experiencing more panic attacks, severe anxiety, and visual problems fairly rapidly over the next year or two after losing her sense of smell. More physical coordination issues started to show up as well. For example, her tennis serve was off kilter, with her toss going off to the side instead of straight up as it should.

"Ann, make your toss simple," I suggested. "For some reason, you have a bad habit with your motion. Start with your hand higher rather than low and having to bring it around your body."

"No," she replied, shaking her head. "I'll work on it."

Then she would toss the ball and it would be off to one side or the other. She just couldn't toss it straight up with any consistency. She wasn't aware this was even happening, which made her all the more frustrated and increased her stress.

Our friend Claire McCarthy relates an episode that took place on the tennis court that may have been an early indication of the decline that was to come. Annie was playing in a singles match, and upon its conclusion, her opponent mentioned to Claire as she walked off the court that Annie had made several bad calls. Keep in mind tennis at this level depends on the players themselves to act as line judges.

"When the person made that comment, it just struck me because that didn't sound like Annie at all," Claire recalls. "She was always very kind and careful with her calls. It wasn't until a few years later that I thought Parkinson's might have been the problem that day."

Another of our tennis friends, Sharon Hartmann, also noticed a decline in Annie's tennis abilities prior to her Parkinson's diagnosis.

"Annie was an incredible tennis player," Sharon says. "We would play whenever we could and she was always a step ahead of me.

"I would notice that I'd hit the ball and she would hesitate. Then she'd swing, but by then the ball would be past her. When I look back, I say, 'Oh, that's what it was. I just thought it was my lucky day on the tennis court.' The decline in her tennis abilities was gradual, but eventually we all knew there was something wrong. She was frustrated, and we didn't know what was causing it.

"One day, Annie realized things weren't going the way she wanted them to go. She said, 'I think I should stop playing tennis.' I told her, 'I'll play with you until you don't want to anymore.' Finally, she just decided her hand-eye coordination wasn't there anymore. She wanted to keep playing, but just couldn't."

Balance started to become more of an issue, too. We were hitting balls together one day when all of a sudden it was if someone had put a lasso around both of her ankles and she went down. It wasn't just that she tripped. I thought, "Oh my God! That was abnormal."

Annie admitted to having some visual problems as well, most noticeably on the tennis court and while driving.

"It's like there are two roads overlapping in front of me," she said. "I'll go around the corner and almost end up on the curb."

I thought she was merely having a panic attack, but now I understand the disease likely was affecting the occipital lobes (vision area) of her brain. The scientific term is visuospatial dysgnosia, also known as visual spatial impairment. Her visual and smelling issues likely were due to the buildup of Lewy bodies in the brain. We had her vision checked out and there was nothing wrong with her eyes. It was a case of her brain not interpreting correctly what she was seeing.

"You've got to be safe, Honey," I said.

"I am," she assured me.

Her vision didn't seem to be a major problem for a while because she didn't complain about it. I didn't ask because I didn't think she was having trouble. Plus, I was trying not to make a big issue out of things. I figured it probably wasn't much worse than my own condition in which I have difficultly recognizing familiar faces. I'll see people and know I should know them, but I don't have a clue how. Then I'll see them in a different context and I'll recognize them right away.

Annie's undiagnosis period, as I refer to it, was stressful for her and we didn't know how to deal with it. She would wonder what was wrong with her – even telling people as much – and became more depressed. We saw a couple of psychiatrists over the next several years as her depression became more pronounced. She didn't want to see anyone locally because she was concerned about people seeing her, so we traveled to see psychiatrists in other cities throughout northeast Wisconsin.

The onset of her depression was gradual in the beginning. I remember visiting one psychiatrist who asked fairly probing, personal questions. Annie cried and then I cried. I felt Annie was reactively becoming depressed as a result of her heightened anxiety, but now I realize there was more to it than that. She took anti-depressant medications for many years to help even out her mood, but when she was down, she cried a lot. One of the major issues that contributed to her depression was the fact she couldn't play tennis anymore. This was an activity that had been therapeutic for her. She found other activities to do, but nothing was ever quite the same as tennis.

The two of us were good examples of how the mental challenges of Parkinson's disease can sneak up on you. Very rarely does something happen suddenly, like is the case with a stroke. Most of the time, changes in personality and general mood are more subtle. There are times, however, where something happens that makes you say, "Oh my God."

The impact of external issues

We would learn much later the significant effects that other life and health events had on Annie's early Parkinson's symptoms during this period. There were things that, in and of themselves, may or may not have had a major impact, but collectively there is no question they produced a crushing effect.

The most obvious factors during this period involved our kids. One by one, they were graduating from high school and leaving for college. The first to leave was Susan. Annie and I both sobbed after helping her move into her dorm at UW-Madison in 1984. Three years later, Sarah headed out to Stanford University. Leaving Susan in Madison was bad enough, even though it was only about two hours away, but flying home alone from the San Francisco Bay Area without Sarah was really tough. Andy was still home, but boys are different than girls. When he went off to the University of Kansas in the fall of 1989, we were now officially empty nesters. This was really difficult on Annie and seemed to intensify her anxiety issues and depression.

Spring of 1989 was the beginning of an extremely eventful year for us. Annie had experienced some menopausal vaginal bleeding while we were vacationing at Siesta Key in Florida, and she would eventually undergo a hysterectomy in May. She was in her late forties and had a lot of stress regarding the operation, so much so that she shook badly while signing the authorization form.

Enjoying Wimbledon in London with our friends Claire and Chuck McCarthy, summer 1989.

"What's wrong with me?" she said. "I can't even write my name!"

Annie had convinced herself she wouldn't survive the operation. Looking back, I can see clearly that her condition began deteriorating quickly at this point. Her Parkinson's symptoms were becoming more significant, but we still hadn't pinned down that diagnosis yet.

We made big plans for our twenty-fifth anniversary that summer, which was a great opportunity to shift our focus back to something positive. The highlight was a trip to England in late June for the Wimbledon tennis tournament with our good friends Chuck and Claire McCarthy. We went with a larger tour that included our airline tickets, tickets to the tournament, and hotel accommodations. Wimbledon is one of the four Grand Slam events held every year. It is a huge deal in the tennis world, and Annie truly enjoyed attending the event as a tennis fan. We took a bus tour out of London one day to see Oxford University and other sights, and on two nights we saw great stage shows. Chuck had some connections that resulted in front-row center seats to *Les Miserables* and second-row seats to *Phantom of the Opera* (right underneath the chandelier that crashes down).

We had all we could do to make it to the theater in time for *Les Mis*. The London Tube (subway) operators were on strike for two days and our hotel was three miles away. The roads were jammed with cars as a result, and there weren't enough taxis to take care of all the people who otherwise would take the Tube. Cellular technology was not reality yet, so we had no easy way to communicate with Chuck and Claire, who were staying a half-mile away from us.

I was trying to hail a taxi (there was no Uber at this time, either) as Annie stood in the front doorway of the hotel in case Claire tried calling the front desk. All of a sudden, a normal-looking car (not a taxi) pulled up, and Chuck was in the backseat. Somehow he had convinced a local resident to serve as our driver. We all hopped in and the driver took off for the theater. In his haste to get us there on time, he went down alleys and the wrong way on one-way streets.

The first song had just started when we rushed to the door, only to have the usher hold us in the back of the theater until the first two songs were done. Then he rushed us down to our seats and we were able to enjoy the rest of the show from up close.

Afterward, that same driver picked us up again. We told him we were hungry, and he said, "I'll take you someplace."

We ended up at some private club, and he argued with the doorman to get us in.

"I'll pick you up in an hour," he said, and then hit a parked car on his way out.

True to his word, he was there when we finished eating and took both couples back to their respective hotels. What an experience!

We had a great time on this trip for the most part. We loved just sitting outside at a table, hanging out and people watching. However, Annie developed a urinary tract infection (UTI) while we were in London, which made her Parkinson's symptoms a lot worse. UTIs seem to accelerate the symptoms of Parkinson's. We didn't yet know that she had Parkinson's disease, but I had my suspicions.

We walked into a doctor's office around the corner from our hotel. I told him that Annie had a recent hysterectomy and was suffering from a probable urinary tract infection. With the understanding that I was a physician and qualified to care for her, he gave us a bottle of antibiotics.

"How much do we owe you?" I asked him.

"It's a present for our good American friends," he said. "I hope you have a good time watching the tennis."

Annie did improve after that and we enjoyed the remainder of our twelve-day trip. Travel is always a little stressful, which is not a good thing for someone with Parkinson's – and in Annie's case, not yet diagnosed – but she did pretty well.

We were thrilled when our kids threw us a surprise twenty-fifth anniversary party midway through July 1989. My parents were there, four couples who were good friends of ours arrived, and the kids arranged to have a catered dinner served. The next week, we drove over to Minneapolis to watch our favorite singer, Neil Diamond, for the first time. Overall, we had a good summer, but a storm was on the horizon.

Empty nest syndrome definitely was taking its toll on Annie during the fall of 1989. Susan was in Madison, Andy was at the University of Kansas, and Sarah was at Stanford in California, so they were not close to home at all. On top of that, this was Annie's last season as tennis coach at St. Joseph Academy (Green Bay's all-girls high school) and her mother was declining rapidly in a Minneapolis nursing home. The burden of all these issues kept building as the hectic Christmas season approached.

Annie was excited for the kids to come home, but feeling stressed because there were holiday plans to be made and the house would be full again. Ominously, she was beginning to exhibit more difficulties with her motor functions. Her non-motor function challenges, such as depression and loss of smell, were not generally acknowledged as Parkinson's symptoms then, but they are now.

Time to face the obvious

It wasn't until that Christmas – thirteen years after Annie first lost her sense of smell – that I finally discussed the potential of Parkinson's disease with a physician acquaintance, Dr. Bob Johnston. Bob was an internal medicine specialist who was known as the doctors' doctor in the Green Bay area. He had observed Annie at a Christmas party we attended at the downtown Green Bay convention center, and he was concerned with what he saw. She was forty-nine years old and her physical symptoms were becoming more apparent.

"Rolf, I saw Ann at the Christmas party last night," Bob said to me. "She's got Parkinson's."

"I know," I replied.

"You should not tell her," he said. "I should tell her."

We arranged to meet with Bob in his office at five o'clock on New Year's Eve. Ann was no dummy. She knew something was up.

"Ann," Bob said, getting right to the point. "I saw you at the Christmas party and watched how you were moving. I don't think there is any doubt but that you have Parkinson's disease."

He went on to describe Parkinson's for us, and how there are lots of medications and other kinds of treatments suggested by the medical community.

"We will have you see a neurologist, and I'll be glad to help you out as needed," he concluded. "You can feel free to come see me whenever you want. Do you have any questions?"

Annie replied that she did not, although I'm sure her head was spinning with a combination of emotion and panic so intense that it made thinking clearly in that moment a virtual impossibility. We left his office, got back in the car, and then she just melted down, as did I. She sobbed and I sobbed. I hugged her.

"My life is over," she said. "I've had to give up tennis. I'm never going to get to see our kids get married. I'm never going to see our grandkids."

She was hitting on all the things important to her. Tennis she could live without, but the kids and grandkids she could not.

I snuggled up to her and said, "Annie, I love you dearly. I always have and I always will. I will be with you forever, and we will always be in our own home. The enemy is Parkinson's disease. It's not your fault and it's not my fault. I will be there for you, our kids will be there for you, and our friends will be there for you. I know you so well and I know how tough you are, and I know that you will fight this. We are going to fight this damn disease, and we are going to make a difference. You *will* see our kids get married. You *will* get to see our grandchildren. We *will* make a difference."

I had not rehearsed that response. It came from my heart in the moment as we both cried. As it turned out, we were able to actively fight this disease for thirty-one more years. When Annie slept away at eighty and a half years old, God had guided her through her battle against Parkinson's disease for at least forty-five years. She had seen our three kids get married and we had eight grandchildren, the youngest of whom was eleven and the three oldest were in college.

I told Annie's college friend, Shindy, about Annie's meltdown while talking to her during the writing of this book.

"That doesn't surprise me one bit," she said. "When she would get bad news, she would think the world was ending. The next day, she would take charge."

That is consistent with how Annie handled her situation the rest of her life. I never heard her say "Why me?" in all the years of her journey. In fact, the very next morning after speaking with Dr. Johnston, New Year's Day 1990, she stated, "I hate this damn disease," and immediately put all of her energy into fighting it. There was never any doubt that she would be in our home for the duration of her journey.

Family histories to consider

Family history plays varied roles when it comes to medical risk factors for all of us. Some diseases, such as breast cancer, have shown direct connections to the probability of future generations developing the affliction. The relationship is not as profound with some other diseases, such as Parkinson's. Annie's mother, Zita, likely had Parkinson's, and her brother, Buzz, actually did receive a Parkinson's diagnosis. Their health issues were red flags that certainly were not lost on Annie.

Zita was essentially vegetative for the last two years of her life. We would often see her slumped in a chair and unresponsive. No wonder Annie panicked when she received her own Parkinson's diagnosis.

"I'm going to end up just like my mother," she said many times.

"Ann, your mother's doctors say she does not have Parkinson's disease," I would counter.

Zita, who died in 1992, had Lewy body disease of the brain. This may or may not have been Parkinson's. It's a gray area separating the two. I used that potential difference as a calculated lie to help calm Annie's fears.

Things were no better for Annie in looking at my family. My dad had terminal liver disease and my mother had Alzheimer's disease. They died ten days apart in 1991, a year prior to Zita's passing. My brother, Kim, died of Alzheimer's disease in 2021.

We moved my parents from Dodgeville up to Green Bay so we could take a more active role in their care, and Kim was only about a half-

Annie (right) with her sister, Kathy ("Sis"), and brother, Albert Jr. ("Buzz"), 1987.

hour away in Appleton. Our dad immediately went into the hospital while our mother lived at the house with us for ten days until we could get her placed in a memory care facility. I knew the time had come for both of them. It was the blessings of God saying, "The end is here." They were never going to have a quality of life again.

My dad went relatively quickly, passing away in a sedated state of sleep. Kim and I visited our mother together the next day to inform her that Dad had died.

"Mom, we have some sad news," I said. "Dad died last night."

"Did he have a girlfriend?" she asked.

"You were the only girlfriend he ever had," I replied.

"Oh," she said.

Annie and I went to visit her the following Sunday and brought along some lemon bars that Annie had made. My mom had not been eating well and was skinny as could be. She held up one of the bars and just looked at it.

"You need to eat this, Grandma," Annie said. "You're getting too skinny."

"You should talk, Skinny!" my mom replied as all three of us roared with laughter. It was a nice moment.

Before we left, my mom said, "I'm ready to go home."

I don't think she was referring to her house in Dodgeville.

I woke up at about five o'clock the next morning and just had a bad feeling about my mother. I figured I'd stop in to see her on my way to the Rotary Club breakfast. Before I left the house, I called the nurse on duty to check on her.

"Dr. Lulloff, I was just going to call you," the nurse said. "I just walked into your mother's room, and she has passed away."

I found out later that Kim's daughter, Keri, who was a student at UW-Madison, also woke up that morning and couldn't get her grandmother out of her mind. It was goose bumps-type of stuff, but it also may have soothed Annie's fears a bit in seeing how relatively peaceful an end-of-life journey could be.

There is no doubt that Annie was my care partner and I was her care partner, just in different ways.

Observing Annie's decline from other perspectives

Conditions such as Parkinson's disease reveal themselves differently to different people. Our family was no different, especially since Annie's early symptoms were not readily apparent. Our kids experienced varying levels of realization when it came to their mother's health. I'll let them describe it in their own words:

Susan

"My mom was stubborn. I didn't see any signs of Parkinson's because I don't think she wanted it to interfere with her life. I remember my mom had to have a spinal tap when I was about thirteen or fourteen. I'm sure it was related to all the things going on with her, but I just knew she wasn't feeling good. She had to be in a reclined position for several days. She drove me to the grocery store to shop, and then laid down in the car while I went inside. I didn't even know how to write a check, and I did it wrong.

"Especially when looking at pictures now, I see that she really wasn't doing well as time went on. She needed help with her balance. My husband remembers at our wedding that he went to dance with her and she was very nervous about falling."

Sarah

"I didn't notice any symptoms until I came home after my freshman year of college in 1988. We walked together several times that summer, and I noticed her arms weren't swinging like normal. 'Mom, swing your arms!' I said, without realizing it was not something within her control. That was the first motor symptom I noticed, and I think she voiced having a little trouble playing tennis then, too.

"She did have a mess of psychological things happening as well as physical. Migraine headaches came out of the blue, and the first time I noticed depression was in the fall of 1989. She had a hysterectomy done that spring, and her mood seemed out of proportion. That really struck me. I felt badly for her that she seemed so emotional, and I didn't understand. She had a lot of things happening about that time. Her kids were leaving for college; menopause was happening; she was losing her identity as a mother, and that had been her job for a number of years.

"Our mom was always kind of a tough cookie. She didn't put up with any B.S. from us kids. But she also was a softie and affectionate. She powered through things. I didn't view her as somebody who dwelled on things, but once her diagnosis hit, she had a lot of emotion over the loss of the ability to do some of the things she wanted to do. I felt like she just had this feeling of despair, hopelessness, and helplessness.

"As a young adult trying to support her, I didn't have a whole lot of tools in my toolkit at that point. I tried to listen and hugged her. I remember saying, 'Mom, I can't imagine what you're going through. It's dreadful, but the silver lining is you are surrounded by a family that immensely loves you, and you have friends who love you and care about you. Know that we are here for you no matter what.'

"Despite her knowing that, she was often inconsolable. It was difficult to see that. Her own mother had been in ill health for probably fifteen years – likely with undiagnosed Parkinson's disease – and our mother struggled to see her in that condition. She said repeatedly, 'I know I'm going to end up just like my mother.' She actually said that long before her own diagnosis. She had that fear.

"I had not pictured my mother as somebody so vulnerable before. She was a strong person, and this was so out of character. When you're younger, you don't view your parents as having these complex emotions and experiences."

Andy

"I was just a typical high school kid, where all you really want to do is get out of the house and hang out with your friends. I was oblivious to everything. There were two episodes that stick out for me. The first was our mom had a Nissan sports car with a manual transmission. She shifted so slowly and I wondered why. I said, 'Punch it, Mom!' But her hands just didn't move very fast. The second was much later, when we realized that she finally was cognitively declining. We all showed up for Christmas and there wasn't enough food. My sisters said, 'Mom, you didn't make anything.' We knew something was not right."

***

I was always open with the kids about their mother's condition, although we were careful not to agitate Annie because we were aware of how sensitive she tended to be. The most important thing was for the kids to involve us in their families' activities. We froze our butts off at more soccer matches and late-season cross country meets in which our grandkids were participants, but Annie was always a good sport about

On our way to a theme party in about 1980.

it. I would get her all bundled up and move her around in a wheelchair so she could see things when mobility became an issue. We celebrated birthdays, weddings, and other get-togethers as often as possible.

Susan felt left out to a certain degree from her location in Kansas City. Sarah is a straight shooter who has a logical mind. Andy understood the challenges, but came at things from a different perspective as a son rather than a daughter. He calls things the way they are and has the common sense not to throw kerosene on the fire.

We also informed friends of our situation as appropriate. People would come up to me and ask how we were doing as news of her diagnosis spread through the grapevine. There were no secrets. Now, did I publicize it? No, but I didn't hide it, either.

"Rolf, I understand what you're going through," some people would say to me. "Are you okay?"

"Yes, I'm fine," I would respond. "Ann just needs support and love, and we're going to keep on going. We're challenged, but the enemy is the disease. Ann is amazing in her ability to persevere, and we're blessed in that we have the opportunity to gain knowledge in what to do."

Although it was no surprise that Annie was going to be tough, she was human, too. We would break down and cry. That's all part of dealing with life. I needed her just as much as she needed me. You can't be afraid of the tears, because tears are part of the journey. However, those tears help strengthen your love and adapt to what's going on.

Relationships are so important in a journey such as the one we faced with Parkinson's disease. Relationships between spouses, with your kids, and with your friends are all crucial to maintaining your emotional and mental health. We learned to be careful about how we did things as her disease progressed, and everyone was really good about accommodating us.

I knew our challenges would intensify going forward. Our only choice was to work as a team, meet those challenges head on, and live our best lives possible.

Chapter 3

How Our Bodies Work

While my objective in writing this book is to share experiences and learnings for the benefit of families going through neurodegenerative disease journeys, a brief explanation is appropriate here to explain a little bit about how the brain and our bodies work together. I will do my best to keep this easy to understand despite a few terms that may be new to you.

Our brains are among the most complex structures in the universe. They are amazing in their power, and the scientific community is relatively early in its understanding of the brain's various functions compared to less-complex parts of the body. When it comes to understanding how the body works (or doesn't), it is important to visualize how anatomy leads into function and how things do or do not work properly. From there, we can investigate what is interfering with various functions or processes.

We need to have all parts of our brain functioning well in order to live our best quality of life. The brain communicates with itself and other parts of the body in a manner similar to how a computer shares information and commands with downloaded programs or remote computers in a network. The desired action cannot take place when there is a disconnection or obstruction in the network, whether that is inside a computer or our brain.

The human brain has developed over the past several million years in response to the world around us. We have benefitted from a series of tiny mutations over time that have separated us from other animals, particularly regarding the outermost layer of our brain, called the cerebral cortex. This is the part of the brain that lets us think and reason at a high level.

Our brain weighs approximately three pounds. A thick, boney skull protects it from harm in most situations, but it is very fragile. Brain matter is soft and mushy, so it is prone to damage from injuries such as concussions. Many blood vessels supply the nutrition and oxygen the brain needs to function and carry away the waste products generated by the normal metabolism that occurs there.

Our brain contains about ninety billion neurons that produce a constant flurry of chemical interactions and electrical charges to communicate information and commands. Neurons help us do everything from think to move, balance, speak, learn, understand, and process information from our senses. Neurodegenerative diseases such as Parkinson's develop when neurons or associated nervous systems progressively lose function over time.

Each neuron sends out messages through what's called an axon, and each axon connects with hundreds or even thousands of other nerve cells at receptacles called dendrites. Every single thought, memory, conscious action, and unconscious action we have takes place as a result of activity in our neurons.

Our neural pathways are long and complex, and any number of issues can disrupt the communication channels within them. Obstructions in the form of abnormal protein clumps can affect the ability of cells to communicate with each other. These faulty connections act similarly to a computer that no longer can execute a program. Something has been corrupted along the way. Unfortunately, we can't simply reboot our brains or reinstall a program.

Although our brains are very active, they do have limited capacity. We can't remember everything. Our brains select what is worth saving in memory and what is not, as frustrating as that may be when you struggle to remember someone's name when you see them in a store. Neurons have basic functions as well as specialty functions depending on which part of the brain is involved. Thanks to our autonomic nervous system, we don't even have to think about performing actions such as breathing, heartbeat, blood pressure, and many others. They take place automatically, or at least they do in a normally functioning brain.

Unfortunately for Parkinson's patients, it is common to struggle with any number of these automatic functions because of the neural pathway obstructions caused by the disease's signature protein clumps. "Autonomic dysfunction" is a collective term that refers to the body's inability to perform functions that it should be able to do on autopilot. The automatic operations of our bodies, such as body temperature, maintaining a steady pulse and blood pressure, urinary control, bowel control, and heart rate can occasionally go out of whack. When it comes to blood pressure, you can be fine one minute and pass out the next because of a spike or drop in blood pressure.

These types of non-motor symptoms in Parkinson's patients can appear well before or after the onset of the more obvious tremors, and often become more severe as the disease state progresses. They are not constant companions on the journey, but they can rear their ugly head at the most inopportune times. I will share the issues Annie had with autonomic dysfunction later on and discuss the steps we took to counteract them.

On the conscious side of brain activity, we can choose positive thoughts and activities that are good for us and avoid the ones that are bad for us. We have the power to override bad habits and other ingrained tendencies. We can also recover from some brain injuries by retraining our brain and creating new neural pathways through a process called neuroplasticity.

Simply put, neuroplasticity refers to the brain's ability to heal itself – or retrain itself – by modifying existing communication channels (neural pathways). That could mean relearning how to walk correctly, balance correctly, or even swallow correctly. I'll also talk more about neuroplasticity later as it relates to Annie's journey and our focus on maintaining her quality of life.

The main pillars of brain health are nutrition, stimulation, and physical activity. The best thing you can do for your brain is to keep moving, moving, moving! Scientists are taking note of the benefits of exercise. A 2013 research paper (the lead author was Giselle M. Petzinger, MD)

All dressed up for a charity ball about 1983.

reported on studies that showed the positive effects of exercise on neuroplasticity in Parkinson's disease patients.

You don't have to walk all the way around the block, but it's ideal if you can include some level of intensity. Even as Annie's condition deteriorated, we were able to get her onto a NuStep machine for some exercise. We initially had the machine in our basement, and then moved it up to the main level as it became too unsafe for her to use the stairs. I was able to help her up and down the stairs by myself at first, and later with additional help from our caregiving assistant, Sally Ann. That worked well enough until I became worried about what would happen if Annie fell backward and I couldn't catch her. She used that machine up until about six months before she died. She couldn't move much by that point, but we did try to keep using it and I am convinced it had a positive effect.

Every living cell in our body needs nourishment, and brain cells are no exception. In fact, even though our brain comprises only a small percentage of our body's total weight, it burns up approximately twenty percent of our energy. If you have ever wondered why you're so tired after a particularly taxing mental or emotional day, it's because your brain used up a lot of energy to work that hard.

Sleep is the brain's way of taking a timeout and recharging for the next day. It is during sleep that our brains really clean house and get rid of the waste products generated since our last sleep. It's similar to rebooting your computer. The best ways to help your brain are eating healthy foods and getting a good night's sleep. Stay away from poisons and toxins such as alcohol, tobacco products, and dangerous chemicals including weed killers. And as more studies are showing, avoid the repeated head trauma common with some sports.

General brain anatomy 101

Scientists continue to make advances in mapping the specific functions performed within the various parts of the brain. There are four regions on both sides of your head called lobes. Let's take a quick tour of your brain.

Starting up front, the aptly named **frontal lobes** are the largest lobes of the brain. They are involved in decision-making capabilities, voluntary movements, expressive language, personality characteristics, and higher-level executive functions such as reasoning and problem solving.

Moving backward over the top of your head, the next major areas are the **parietal lobes**. These lobes take care of managing our senses, including interpretation of input it receives from other areas of the body, and they help us speak and understand language.

The **occipital lobes**, located on the back of the brain, are responsible for our visual perception. Damage to the neurons here can present itself in having difficulty locating objects. This may have accounted for Annie's problems with her tennis serve and inconsistent driving vision.

The **temporal lobes** are located on the sides of our head, just behind our ears. These areas are involved with processing auditory information, short-term memory, speech, and possibly smell recognition.

Another critical area of the brain, known as the **cerebellum**, is located at the back of the head below the occipital lobes. It is responsible for muscle control, including balance and movement, and also plays an important role in language processing and memory. This area contains the most neurons of any part of the brain.

The structures of the limbic system are located deep in the middle of our brain, just above the brainstem. As the communications center for brain messaging, this is where our brain receives messages, modifies them, and sends out instructions to other parts of the brain for further action or interpretation. The amygdala, which controls emotions, emotional behavior, and motivation is a key structure within the limbic system.

What causes neurodegenerative diseases?

Parkinson's disease, like many brain disorders, produces symptoms that slowly appear and increase in severity as the disorder quietly goes about its business of damaging the brain. The exact symptoms that develop depend on which part of the brain is experiencing damage and to what extent. Many symptoms result from issues in more than one location that are interconnected.

Researchers believe most neurodegenerative diseases are the result of the inability of neurons to function correctly due to interference from abnormal proteins. What causes proteins to develop abnormally is not as yet clearly understood. Likely it is a combination of factors, including exposure to some types of toxin, damage caused by concussion or repeated head trauma, a genetic predisposition, or even simple aging. A single neuron may connect to hundreds, even thousands, of other neurons. They send messages back and forth and across different parts of the brain, working together to create an awareness of what's going on around us.

Different proteins are associated with the various neurodegenerative diseases including Parkinson's, Alzheimer's, ALS (Lou Gehrig's disease) and Huntington's disease. Alpha-synuclein is the protein associated with Parkinson's disease. Research shows this protein twists into clumps called Lewy bodies, which then affects the ability of neurons to function properly. Picture a garden hose and how a kink in it can prevent water from passing through. In our brains, messages can't get through if twisted proteins are clogging up the ability of cells to transmit information.

Lewy bodies and other abnormal proteins can be toxic, and they appear to pass from one neuron to another as the disease state spreads to other parts of the brain. Ultimate testing on Annie's brain showed that Lewy body buildup was present in areas that controlled her sense of smell and contributed to her mood and memory issues, as well as her movement disorders.

Annie's symptoms began with her loss of smell and then progressed from there. It's also possible her symptoms began much earlier than that when we take into account her friends' reports of her heightened anxiety in college. Assuming her loss of smell involved Lewy bodies, is it possible people who experience this symptom with regard to COVID have a future that includes a neurodegenerative disease? As of this writing, it's too soon to know.

Parkinson's disease frequently includes muscle tremors and other uncontrollable movements eventually, along with slowness and stiffness of movement. This likely is because an area of the midbrain, called the substantia nigra, is no longer capable of producing a neurotransmitter called dopamine due to abnormal protein buildup. The nervous system uses dopamine to send messages between nerve cells. As the level of dopamine goes down, so does the brain's ability to control muscle impulses. This leads to the movement issues associated with Parkinson's disease.

Dementia and hallucinations become common with Parkinson's patients as the increasing effect of Lewy bodies takes its toll on the brain's ability to reason. As care partners, we have to learn to go with the flow

Annie and me enjoying a day with family in our backyard, July 2016.

rather than argue or try to correct what our care person is saying. Logic often will not work and actually can be counterproductive.

For example, I walked into the bedroom one morning to check on Annie and she asked, "Is Mother up?"

"Whose mother?" I asked.

"My mother," she stated, confused as to why I would be asking such a question.

"Ann, your mother has been dead for eleven years."

She looked at me with anger and said, "She is not dead!"

I was inexperienced enough at that time to go find her mother's death certificate and show it to her.

"Oh," was her response.

I looked up delusions and hallucinations right away, and learned they are prevalent with Parkinson's disease. This was my first experience with Annie having them.

"Rolf, you dummy," I thought. "Her brain says that her mother is still alive. Don't create a new problem by fighting her on this."

I got a chance to show what I had learned a few days later.

"Is Mother up?" Annie asked again.

"No, she's still sleeping," I replied.

I had learned not to throw kerosene on the fire. Later on in our journey, I adjusted my answer a little more.

"Is Mother up yet?"

"She's sleeping peacefully in heaven."

Annie never got mad at me for that answer.

Non-motor symptoms and Parkinson's disease

Annie's journey provides a clear example of how Parkinson's disease can display itself outside of the well-known tremors and halting gait for which it is best known. Doctors and therapists refer to these visibly observable issues collectively as motor symptoms because they involve issues with body movement.

There is a whole other set of non-motor symptoms that Annie and most other people dealing with Parkinson's encounter at various points in their journey. Many of these symptoms still involve issues with brain function, but some can extend to other parts of the body.

It is common to experience issues with the senses of sight and smell because the nose and eyes align so closely with nearby regions of the brain. Annie's loss of smell left us confused as to its cause at the time, but in retrospect, it was an obvious early manifestation of Parkinson's taking hold in her brain. Abnormal proteins that develop in the nerves connecting the nose to the brain affect its ability to accurately communicate those sensory signals. Those abnormal proteins stimulate the next piece of the protein down the pathway to twist as well. The effect is similar to a spreading infection, only in this case it is biochemical and involves brain proteins. Eventually, those nerves or the nerve cells in them die from an inability to absorb nutrients from the normal metabolic processes they need to do their job.

Annie's visual problems were most evident when she was driving. She would complain of blurred or double vision, including vertical double vision.

"I'm not sure where the car is headed when I go around the corner," she admitted to me one day.

Annie suffered from terrible panic attacks long before her official diagnosis. I thought it was just general nervousness, and medications seemed to help that. However, we now know that neuropsychiatric issues such as depression, panic attacks, and heightened anxiety can be a precursor to full-blown Parkinson's disease as abnormal proteins begin to build up in that portion of the brain.

The role of our gut in brain health

It may seem odd that the relative health of our gut can play a significant role in brain health, but a growing volume of research indicates that certainly is the case. I'm still building my own understanding of this dynamic. Science never stops and our learning should never stop. This helps us connect more of the dots when it comes to what is important with our brain health.

The latest information as of this writing is that the abnormal deterioration of proteins in the brain differ between the various neurodegenerative diseases (i.e., Alzheimer's, ALS, Parkinson's, chronic wasting disease, and mad cow disease). A key concept is the role of bacteria and similar organisms in our intestinal tract. They not only help us digest what we consume, they also produce some chemicals that are beneficial for our intestinal tract and others that can be damaging.

Evidence is showing that people with Parkinson's disease have certain types of bacteria in their intestinal tract that produce chemicals that can lead to the abnormal protein buildups seen in the nervous system. One study looked at families in which more than one person had Parkinson's disease. The researchers analyzed bacteria from their subjects' stool samples and found that certain types of bacteria were much more common in the people with Parkinson's, yet almost never present in the samples from their spouses. Those bacteria affect certain proteins that then serve as welcome mats into the nervous system for those individuals.

I have seen articles going back as far as the 1990s that proposed Parkinson's disease starts in the gut. Researchers were finding abnormal proteins appearing in nerves in the gut wall, which then stimulated additional proteins in that nerve to twist. The process continued on up the vagus nerve to the base of the brain over about a ten-year period. The vagus nerve is the primary nerve of our parasympathetic nervous system. It controls heart rate and other involuntary (automatic) functions. It is critically important to our overall health and may turn out to be a key component in future Parkinson's research.

Perhaps surprisingly, chronic constipation also can be associated with Parkinson's disease, especially if the person is not drinking enough water or following other dietary best practices to avoid this issue. Parkinson's can feature damaged nerves in the wall of our gut, preventing normal intestinal muscle activity from moving food along the digestive tract for digestion. Annie battled chronic constipation for many years.

It hadn't occurred to me at the time, but Annie's issues going to the bathroom regularly – both urinary and bowel movements – may have originated with Lewy bodies in her gut. Her urinary issues involved incontinence and she did not have bowel movements as often as desired, often only about three times per week. She didn't complain about any of it, simply assuming that's the way her body worked.

The nose is actually part of the gastrointestinal (GI) tract. Those same Lewy bodies that affected the inner workings of Annie's brain also affected the sensory nerves in her nose. The distance from the smelling receptors in your nose to your brain is not far. It is a good example of how everything in our bodies, especially our nervous systems, are connected somehow.

Annie's journey started with a loss of sense of smell and panic attacks, progressed to depression and apathy, the onset of problems with her autonomic nervous system, and the more obvious physical limitations of balance, tremors, slow movement, rigidity, and stiffness. All of these made it apparent that her clinical diagnosis was Parkinson's disease.

Chapter 4

Adapting to Gradual Decline

The official diagnosis hit Annie like a ton of bricks. The devastation that comes with an official diagnosis is real, and that is where having a capable care partner and strong support system are critical. My primary job as her care partner was as much about motivating and supporting her emotionally as it was about dealing with her expanding physical limitations. It would remain that way for the rest of our journey, but it was especially important in the aftermath of the diagnosis. At least now we knew what we were dealing with. We informed our kids, of course, because they knew something was wrong with Mom.

"I was at work when the phone call came," Susan recalls. "What I thought of Parkinson's was that it was a disease where you shake. I remember thinking, 'At least she doesn't have cancer.' I thought of cancer as having more of a chance that you were going to die. To me,

Parkinson's was a relief because I thought that was something you can live with for a while. I still feel badly I thought this, but I was clueless. I don't remember asking many questions. I was sad she had something, but I also thought, 'Okay, this is something you can live with,' not realizing how horrible of a disease it really is."

I was prepared for the Parkinson's diagnosis, but it was still devastating. Annie was suspicious about her mother's illness perhaps being Parkinson's. In fact, Zita was approaching vegetative status and would pass away two years later. We had gone from the challenges of "undiagnosis" to those of having a diagnosis. It was a relief in a sense, because not knowing was worse than knowing.

Annie and I did not cover up the news about her diagnosis, although we did continue to keep her visits to the psychiatrist private. The stigma that some people associated with mental health at that time was not something she wanted to deal with. The Parkinson's revelation was uncomfortable to talk about at first. It didn't take long until the news became gossip, quickly making its way around the medical and tennis communities.

Maintaining friendships and participating in social activities are so important in a journey like ours. The burden may fall more on the care partner as the decline progresses, although Annie was very good about staying active long into her journey. It can be tempting for either or both of you to retreat into your darkness – and few people would fault you for that – but your mental health and that of your care partner depend on staying open to the world. We would go for walks on local trails and in parks that had nicely spaced benches we could access as needed, which was a nice change of scenery from walking around our neighborhood.

Annie and I enjoyed long-term friendships with a number of groups of people. Our Badger alumni group, comprised of University of Wisconsin grads like us, continues to get together and bond. About one-third of our alumni group had a connection to my hometown of Dodgeville, Wisconsin. We either knew each other from high school or became friends with via the domino effect in college, where friends, girlfriends, or roommates of people we knew integrated into our group.

We purchased four season tickets in 1994 to the Badgers' football games so we could take friends with us. There were at least eight different couples with whom we enjoyed fun weekends. As many seasons as Annie was able, we would go down to Madison on a Friday, find a fish fry for dinner, and head down to campus. After the game, we'd stick around for the Fifth Quarter (the post-game show put on by the marching band), then go over to State Street and have a nice dinner, often at Paisan's.

Our tennis friends also were very important. Along with people in the medical community, our tennis friends were the first people we met when we moved to Green Bay. Annie went over to Green Isle Park shortly after we moved to our first house in Allouez and introduced herself to the women playing on the courts there. Bingo, she had people to play with!

One of the first motor skills affected by her Parkinson's was the loss of her ability to play tennis. This had a major impact on her, because the sport was such a significant part of her life for many years. Not only was she an excellent player in her own right, she coached the St. Joseph Academy girls for four years (1986-89). Sarah developed into an excellent player during this time, even winning the WISAA (private schools) state championship as a senior in 1987.

"After her diagnosis, her emotional state was a roller coaster," Sarah observes. "It was the start of a series of losses for her. First was the loss of tennis, a lifelong activity that she loved. It was the basis for many friendships, she planned her calendar around it, and it was at least one of her communities. In the process of losing the ability to play like she did, she lost some of that camaraderie. She lost that outlet for pushing herself, and she had enjoyed that kind of athleticism."

Life was more than tennis to Annie, but it certainly was a priority. One day, she was really upset about not being able to play tennis anymore. She got all her trophies, put them in a box, and told me to drop them in the trash.

"You don't want to do that," I said, trying to calm her down.

"Yes, put them in the trash!" she ordered.

I don't know if she ever knew, but I put them in the basement instead.

Annie's college friend, Shindy, said Annie's level of optimism understandably became more difficult to maintain as her physical symptoms began to affect her quality of life.

"The hardest blow came when she was moving up the ladder in the senior division of tennis and was diagnosed with Parkinson's disease, especially at such an early age," Shindy said. "She would get furious about all the medication she was on and that it was not enabling her to live a relatively normal life. I think when an athlete is struck down at an early age, it is much harder for them to accept that a disease can limit their activity. I don't think acceptance of her limitation came easily, but she eventually accepted the challenges of her 'new' everyday life and endeavored to live as normally as she could."

The decade of the 1990s was our first dealing with an official diagnosis of Parkinson's disease, and the life changes that were in full swing the previous year showed no signs of slowing down. Annie and I were determined not to let that damn disease slow us down, either. In fact, counting our 1989 trip to London and Wimbledon for our twenty-fifth anniversary, we ended up taking multiple trips to Europe and the Caribbean during this period.

Here we are at the surprise party our children arranged on the occasion of our twenty-fifth wedding anniversary in July 1989, less than six months before Annie's official Parkinson's diagnosis.

Sarah was planning to spend her spring quarter of 1990 at Stanford's campus in Tours, France, which is about 150 miles southwest of Paris. Following that, she had plans to stay in Europe for the summer doing tropical disease research for the World Health Organization in Geneva, Switzerland. We were not going to go six months without seeing Sarah, so Annie and I made arrangements to travel to Europe.

We flew into Paris and spent two days there at Sarah's urging. We rented a car and drove up to Normandy, where we saw the museum honoring the D-Day invasion. It was a real tear-jerker. After meeting up with Sarah in Tours and spending two nights there, the three of us went down to the Riviera and stayed three nights in Nice. We then went to Geneva to help Sarah find a place to live, and she eventually rented a room from an older couple in their house. Then we returned to Paris, where there was a big celebration in the streets the night we arrived to mark the summer solstice. Music and partying took place all night long.

In the stands at the US Open Tennis Championships with Tom and Jean Badciong, ready for the big Jimmy Connors vs. Patrick McEnroe match in August 1991.

Annie traveled well throughout all of this and didn't have any significant challenges. We really had a great trip.

Our other two children were on the move during this period as well. Andy transferred from the University of Kansas to UW-Madison for the fall semester, while Susan took a job in Kansas near one of her high school friends.

In 1991, our whole family went out to California for Sarah's graduation from Stanford in May, and we visited Yosemite National Park for four days while we were there. Sarah remained at Stanford for the following academic year, taking more classes and working as a teaching assistant (TA).

Tennis continued to provide a welcome diversion, even though Annie wasn't playing anymore. She transitioned to golf for social purposes, but it didn't take long until her Parkinson's made that activity too difficult as well. In August 1991, we went to New York for the US Open Tennis Championships with our friends Tom and Jean Badciong. The trip was memorable for an incident in which we were able to "talk to a guy" who helped us secure unused corporate seats in the front row for the highly anticipated Jimmy Connors vs. Patrick McEnroe match rather than use the tickets we had in the nosebleed section. That was so much fun!

Travel provided a welcome escape. We visited Germany, Austria, and Switzerland in 1992. We flew into Frankfurt, Germany, and rented a car for our adventure. We started in the ancient city of Rothenburg for three nights. They celebrate beer drinking there like you can't believe, and this coming from someone who lives in Wisconsin!

From there, we visited the site of the Dachau concentration camp, which was very sad and emotional. We also saw Munich and entered Austria to tour Vienna, where we got the opportunity to see the famous Vienna Boys Choir. We also did a castle tour, visited a German ski village in the Alps for three days, and stayed in Heidelberg for two nights. It was a great trip and Annie fared quite well.

We told the kids that 1993 would be their one chance to see Europe with us, on us. They all took us up on the offer, and we spent the second half of May with them in Germany, France, and Switzerland. We had a great time. Unfortunately, I had been working hard and was exhausted, and came down with a bad cold. Thankfully, I did recover quickly. We

Enjoying the Irish countryside during our visit in 1995.

spent five days in Paris, two days in the French wine country, and four days in Lauterbrunnen, an enchanting small town in the Swiss Alps. While in France, we toured castles, saw Monet's house, and just hung out.

It would turn out to be our last family vacation with just the five us, without any spouses, significant others or grandchildren. Sarah, who had earned her master's degree in public health from UW-Madison earlier that month, began her medical school journey two months later at the Medical College of Wisconsin in Milwaukee. She would go on to earn her MD and is now an infectious disease specialist in Green Bay.

Andrew graduated from UW-Madison in May of 1994 and announced he wanted to become a dentist. This surprised us, but he had done his homework and was ready for the challenge ahead. First, he took a year off to enjoy life in the Colorado skiing and hospitality industry.

In 1995, we traveled to Italy and enjoyed the country by ourselves for a week before meeting up with Jim and Pat Hinckley. Jim was a partner orthopedic surgeon, and he and Pat were longtime friends of ours. August saw a return trip to the US Open in New York, this time with longstanding friends Fred and Sue Hollenbeck.

As time went on, we booked our trips to the US Open through a package service that included transportation. Annie had difficulty getting up the big steps onto a bus, so the woman organizing our group told us to use the next van instead. Well, it turned out to be a limousine, and there were some players inside, including a tall, young Russian woman.

"Good luck tomorrow," I said.

"Thank you," she replied with a big smile.

In June 1996, we enjoyed a bike trip in France for four days with my brother Kim and his wife, Jeannie. We all rode individual bikes and had a good time. Annie did okay. She was borderline safe, and I stayed close to her at all times.

We were trying to improve Annie's mobility for a trip to Europe in 1998, capped off with a few days in Paris at the French Open. We adjusted her medications to get control over her motor symptoms, but one of them caused her terrible nausea. We weren't even able to join our friends at the stadium for a few days. We stopped the medicine and got it out of her system in time to enjoy our last day there. We went on a river cruise on the Seine. It was a beautiful, warm spring night. The Eiffel Tower was spectacular and the food was great. We enjoyed an absolutely idyllic experience.

All told during the 1990s, we enjoyed multiple vacations per year in Florida, made numerous trips to Europe, and twice vacationed in the Caribbean. Those trips were very therapeutic despite the fact they could be stressful. Annie liked to sleep in, so I would give her a kiss and tell her I was going out for a run. We would have breakfast together later in the morning and enjoy the day together.

Annie did fine on her own during much of this period and our lives continued on somewhat normally. We were dealing with the emotional challenges of her disease and there certainly were times she really struggled. However, there were also times when others might not have noticed she even had a disease.

Our Florida change of pace

In 1996, six years after Annie's diagnosis, we made a decision that was somewhat out of character for a couple who prided ourselves on thorough planning: we bought a condominium unit on Sanibel Island in Florida. It turned out to be just the escape we needed and something we could look forward to for many years as kind of a pattern interrupt.

We were staying on nearby Captiva Island during a two-week vacation to Florida in mid-March, and Andy and Sarah were there with us over their college spring breaks. We were renting a condo that was across the hall from our friends Pat and Florence Garland. We drove Andy to the airport at the end of the first week so he could return to dental school. On the way back to Captiva, Annie said, "Let's drive down West Gulf Drive. I just want to see what it's like."

We had never driven down West Gulf Drive before. Condominiums populate this area of neighboring Sanibel Island, so not surprisingly, it wasn't long before we saw a sign for an open house at a new project that featured several buildings.

"Why don't we go take a look at it?" Annie said in a tone carrying more of a statement vibe than an actual question.

"I'm not interested in buying," I replied.

"Neither am I," she said.

So with that, we parked the car, rang the doorbell, and walked inside.

"This place is really nice," Annie said quietly.

The couple showing the unit came out to greet us and asked where we were from. The unit really was nice. It featured three bedrooms, three and a half bathrooms, a family room, dining room, kitchen, and lanai. As new construction, the complex featured updated building codes put in place since the previous hurricane.

"All the units for sale here have the same floor plan, but the third floor units have a circular staircase going onto the roof," one of the agents explained. "The roof features your own fenced-in area to sit and watch the sunsets."

"Can we look at one of those?" we asked. "Are any for sale?"

"Yes, the building in the back of the development looks onto the pool, and you can see out to the ocean between the buildings."

We went back to the building she described and found a completed unit minus the finishing touches. We were able to go up on the roof.

"Is this ever neat!" I said, now caught up in the excitement.

Prices for the units in this building were significantly less than those in the oceanfront buildings. I did some quick math in my head and figured we could actually afford a nicer, third-floor unit in this building and still have a reasonable mortgage.

We went back to Captiva and told Pat and Florence about our adventure.

"You should buy that," Pat said. "That's a damn good price."

We went back the next day with Sarah and watched the sunset on the roof. By the end of the week, we owned that condo. We were in our mid-fifties and had never even had a cottage before. It took about six months to get the unit ready and furnished. It was brand new and we had the opportunity to furnish it to our tastes. We budgeted it out and I told Annie to do it up right. She took charge of the project, flying down to Florida on her own, renting a car, picking out furniture, and arranging for delivery.

That condo was our toy. We went to Sanibel four or five times a year almost every year from 1996 through the spring of 2015. We only drove down there once in all those years, and that was a disaster. Annie's Parkinson's was significant when we made that 1,500-mile drive in 2008. That was not a good decision.

Still, going to our condo was like an extended honeymoon for the first fifteen years we owned it. I was still working full time, so getting out of our routine at home really sparked our love life. It was joyous just being together, especially with me not having to work while we were there. We had learned by this time to hug, love, and live, and Annie defined herself by her quality of life, not by her Parkinson's disease.

While Annie slept in, I would ride my bike over to the general store to get some donuts or sticky buns, and food for the day. We would have breakfast out on the lanai when I returned. After breakfast, we would go down to the beach and walk barefoot through the shallow water.

Having access to our condo made a huge difference in the trajectory of Annie's disease. We now knew what we were dealing with and had medications that could provide her some relief. The biggest challenge was balancing the medications as her body changed.

We rented out the condo during some of the periods when our family wasn't using it the first year, but quickly determined that was not a good situation. This was our home away from home, and we used it enough to average almost sixty nights per year there. We decided, "If we have to rent it out, we shouldn't own it."

We enjoyed our condo for about seventeen years until it became too difficult for Annie to move safely there. She struggled to get up on the roof or walk on the beach the last couple of years, and her travel chair certainly wasn't effective in the sand. We offered it to our kids when we made the decision to sell, but none of them wanted to buy it.

We would go through periods when Annie could not move because her medications had worn off and she was practically frozen in place. I would get her another pill when I would get up during the night. However, I had difficulty awakening her during the night we arrived in the spring of 2012. I tried to get her to open her mouth a little so I could use a spoon to give her a pill with a little bit of water. We also had a squirt bottle that she could use to help wash things down.

On this particular night, she just wasn't responding. Then I made what could have been the most catastrophic move of my life. I squirted a little water from the bottle into her mouth. There was no noise at all coming from her, and then all of a sudden she had a terrible struggle just to breathe. Her color turned ashen and I was panicking.

"Annie, wake up!" I yelled, giving her a little shake to try to arouse her.

There was no response. I was terrified. She wasn't breathing, her pulse was weak, and I feared she might be going into cardiac arrest. I turned her on her side and pounded on her back. I checked her airway and found nothing. Next, I gave her a couple of mouth-to-mouth breaths. I didn't think I had to pump on her chest just yet, since that almost certainly would have resulted in broken ribs.

As those thoughts were flashing through my brain, I heard a low moan. Annie suddenly took a few breaths.

"Oh my God, thank you!" I shouted.

Annie most likely experienced what's called a laryngospasm, which is a protective response by the body when you get water or other substance on your vocal chords. It temporarily makes it very difficult to speak or breathe. As a surgeon, I occasionally would witness that reaction from some of my patients in the recovery room.

Annie seemed okay, but I was concerned she had aspirated. I called 911, which I probably didn't need to do in retrospect. We had her checked out and everything was fine. She didn't seem to have any memory of the incident and suffered no long-term effects from it. Seeing a loved one have a choking episode is just so scary. In fact, this was one of the most trying episodes for me personally. It was an example of how all of us live and learn, even if you have a medical background like I do.

There were no tears when we left the condo for the final time prior to selling it in March 2015. We spent two weeks getting it ready for closing. We hugged and gave thanks for eighteen wonderful honeymoon years there. Not only was it therapeutic for me, it was therapeutic for Annie, too. And it gave our entire family nice memories. But we knew the reality, and it was time to let it go.

A cautionary tale regarding dementia

I happened to run into one of the psychiatrists Annie had seen years earlier and updated him on her progress.

"Rolf, the challenge – which most people don't acknowledge at this point – is the dementia that will come. And it will eventually come," he said. "People usually don't acknowledge that."

I didn't realize dementia was so common with Parkinson's disease, but I thought, "Well, he knows his stuff and I'll pay attention." It did eventually come, but not until she was well into her seventies. And even then, it was more of a comforting type of dementia. It was better that she did not know how miserable she was.

As a family member or spouse, you can see signs of dementia when they begin to occur, although usually it's very a subtle change. A diseased brain often does not function at the level it once had, and Annie's brain was no exception. I learned to agree with her even when I knew deep down that she probably was not correct in whatever she was thinking. But it kept her happy, and that was critically important.

When you have lived with someone as long as I had lived with Annie, I should have known what to do. Don't make things worse and certainly don't make it your loved one's fault. Annie couldn't help it that her brain wasn't working properly. I learned it was better to lie a little when appropriate than cause her unnecessary anxiety.

The ups and downs of living with Parkinson's disease

Parkinson's is not one of those diseases where you all of a sudden find yourself in a terrible place. The up-and-down trajectory of the journey is gradual at times and things do happen suddenly at other times. There is no such thing as a steady decline with Parkinson's. We could go months at a time when things would go well, and then all of a sudden we would have issues with intense emotional instability and visible motor symptoms.

Like many spouses, I would find ways to ignore her depression and the gradual physical deterioration that became very evident in photos. I have included photos in this book that may make it appear as though the changes happened quickly, but in fact they occurred over several decades.

Apathy became more apparent later in Annie's journey, although she remained facially vibrant into her late sixties. She became more withdrawn and was content just to sit in a chair, especially over the final couple of years. Delusions and hallucinations also occurred more often later on as her brain abnormalities took hold. Delusions are when the person interprets something differently than what it actually is. Hallucinations are when the person sees something that's not really there.

There were times when Annie rebelled against her reality as the disease progressed from mild to moderate, and then on to moderately severe. It was perfectly understandable.

"Why is this happening to me?" she would ask almost rhetorically on particularly bad days.

"Annie, it's the goddamn disease," I would say. "We are going to fight it together. Do you realize you've been fighting this damn disease for more than thirty-five years? You are so amazing!"

I'd cry sometimes, too. It's important for your care person to understand that their condition is not their fault. I would give her a big hug. Hugs are so therapeutic, even more so than words alone.

We did as many things as we could to promote and enjoy the ups in our journey. For example, attending sports events was a big thing for us. We were Wisconsin Badgers fans, since Madison is where we met and fell in love, and all three of our children were born there. We vowed that if the football team ever qualified for the Rose Bowl, we were going to go. This was a period in time when the Wisconsin football program was just beginning its rise to prominence after not appearing in the Rose Bowl since 1963. We didn't even know each other then.

Finally, the Badgers had a really good team in 1993 and qualified for

Our family of University of Wisconsin Badgers football fans proudly wore our school's colors at the 1994 Rose Bowl parade and game in Pasadena, California. (From left) Andy, Susan, Annie, Rolf, and Sarah.

the January 1, 1994, Rose Bowl game against UCLA. We took all three kids and joined a tour group that unfortunately did not include game tickets. We were determined to join other fans from around the country and enjoy the experience in Pasadena, California.

Another reason I wanted to go was it would be a rare opportunity to visit Dick Diehl, one of my friends from Fort Dix, New Jersey, where we spent two years in the army. Dick had gone on to practice orthopedic surgery in Pasadena. His impressive home was only a long block away from the stadium and his mother's condominium overlooked the parade route. Dick invited us to join them, and we were able to watch the spectacular Rose Bowl parade from her balcony. As a bonus, he also was able to procure tickets to the game for us!

The game itself was a most memorable experience. We sat in the corner of an end zone where the biggest play of the game took place. I remember yelling, "There's nobody out there!" as UW quarterback Darrell Bevell broke into the clear and ran in what turned out to be the winning touchdown of a 21-16 victory. It was right in front of us.

"My God, we might win!" we yelled over the din of 100,000 spectators.

I tried to keep our lives filled with fun events like this. We likely would have taken many of the adventures we did during our journey anyway. On the other hand, we certainly had a motivation to maximize the time we had while Annie was relatively mobile and well. She was so receptive to all of these events. There is no doubt she did just as much for me, if not more, as I did for her.

We also went to a lot of UW-Green Bay men's basketball games over the years and adapted our routines to Annie's abilities. Toward the end, we would sit in the entryway at court level rather than going up to our seats. There was a handicap-accessible bathroom down underneath the stands that most people didn't know existed. We sat right by the visiting team and enjoyed talking to their fans. We refused to sit around and feel sorry for ourselves, and getting out was certainly therapeutic for me as well.

The ups and downs of the disease would give us a jolt every so often when things didn't go well. I figured we might as well shoot for the moon and see what happens. When it became apparent we weren't going to get to the moon, we transitioned to counting our blessings. This is when you get into the spirituality portion of the journey a little deeper, and the basis of that comes from love. Our goal was to look at our glass being half-full rather than half-empty. We would try to turn every bad day into a good day, every bad moment into a better moment. The manner in which you approach things can have a major impact on your quality of life.

The effectiveness of medications was the biggest variable to Annie's quality of life, especially for the first ten to fifteen years after her diagnosis. She was starting to exhibit symptoms that involved her motor skills, including the tremors commonly associated with Parkinson's. She was taking the combination dopamine replacement drug of carbidopa and levodopa to manage the symptoms. Dopamine is a neurotransmitter naturally produced in the brain that decreases as a result of Parkinson's. Levodopa can cause nausea, but that side effect often eases when taken in combination with carbidopa.

We would go along for a few months just fine, and then all of a sudden, nausea and other side effects would kick in, forcing her to lie down more often at times. Dyskinesias can be another side effect of the medicines that control tremors. Dyskinesia refers to uncontrolled, involuntary movements that may occur with long-term use of levodopa. It is not a symptom of Parkinson's disease itself.

In Annie's case, this side effect resulted in sudden, nervous legs that drove her crazy. She started taking other medications to counteract that. One of them was the prescription medication amitriptyline, often used for mild anxiety and depression. We would have Annie take one tablet as needed and it would usually help. Gradually, however, its effectiveness wore off. She would take two tablets per day, then three per day, then back down to two pills and then one per day. We kept her on anti-depressants the rest of her journey. Sarah had a better sense of her mother's level of depression than I did, and she felt strongly about the benefits of those medications.

It seemed there was always another medicine for us to try. We never knew which would work, and often it seemed that nothing more than the luck of the draw determined her outcomes at any particular time. She would have some good days in which she was very active and seemed pretty "normal," and others that were absolute crap.

The unpredictability and variability of it all was very frustrating for both of us. Annie herself described this in a letter she wrote to her sisters in PEO, which is a women-focused international philanthropic organization. The letter is dated June 15, 1998:

Dear Sisters of Chapter N,

I have not forgotten all of you, although it may seem that way. I'm just struggling with my Parkinson's disease, and it is a struggle. The thing that makes it so difficult is that the disease is never the same two days in a row. It's this way for everyone who has it. On a day when I'm fairly good, I try to do things exactly the same the next day, but I am never the same. One day two pills does a good job of controlling the disease. The next day I may need double the dose, but the tradeoff will be very unpleasant side effects.

In the last six months, three new drugs have been released. I've tried two and had poor results. I'm planning to try the third next week. When I run into someone I know and they ask how I'm doing and I tell them, they say, "But you look so good." For that I'm thankful, because if I looked as bad as I feel, I'd scare people. Enough on that for now.

I want you to know how much I appreciate the many phone calls and the notes you've sent. A sincere thanks to all of you. I'm optimistic that something will help in the near future, and I will return to regular attendance and be a contributing member of my chapter. In the meantime, I love all of you and miss you. Hope to see you soon.

Love, Ann

A friend of ours who was dealing with significant Parkinson's disease had been seeing a nationally known neurologist in Atlanta. He asked us if we wanted to join him on his next flight down and we accepted his invitation. During our visit with this doctor, we told him about the new medication Annie was taking that was designed to minimize the side effects of carbidopa and levodopa. He told us he agreed with this strategy.

About a month later, the neurologist we were seeing locally called us to say we should stop taking that medication because of reports it could cause liver failure. I called the doctor in Atlanta to get his opinion, and he was not overly concerned. However, he confirmed we should stop taking that medication for now. I never put her back on it. I didn't want to take the chance.

People ask me medication questions all the time. There is no easy answer. The objective often centers on replacing the dopamine that is missing in the brain. This is not an exact science. Instead, it is more live and learn because everyone is different. The dosage Annie needed one day was not necessarily what she needed the next. You learn how to understand the ebb and flow of symptoms, and make your own tweaks within the scope of approved care guidelines.

In the fall of 2007, I mentioned to Annie that we hadn't had a party in a long time. I suggested we host an early Christmas party at Oneida Country Club. This was eighteen years after her diagnosis and she already had four of what would be seven back operations.

"We have to celebrate," I said. "Last year at this time, you were in the hospital. Let's celebrate life."

"I'd like that," she said.

Not only did the idea sound good to Annie, it lit a fire under her. She took charge of everything. The menu, the guest list, the works. It was a great distraction for her and amazing to witness.

The year of three weddings

The year 1997 will always be known as the year of the weddings in our family. Those activities kept Annie happily busy, but of course there is no way to get through a year like that without our share of stress. All three of the kids got married from May through August: Sarah on May 3; Susan on June 7; and Andy on August 16. These were very positive events and we celebrated them greatly. You have to enjoy them – whether you are going through a health journey or not – because this is never going to happen again.

Susan was the first to get engaged, and she and Monty picked the first weekend in June for their wedding. Sarah was next. She and her fiancé were planning to move to Salt Lake City to start their medical training in June, so they selected May 3 as their wedding date.

Susan was not pleased. She complained to Annie that Sarah's May wedding would steal the thunder from her June date. By this time, Andy also had proposed to his girlfriend, and they were planning an August wedding. It was family conference time.

"Look," I told the kids. "Dad writes the checks and here's how it's going to be. We're going to celebrate three weddings this year and we're not going to point fingers. We're going to have none of that. Be fore-warned."

With order restored within the family, it was time to focus on the details of these three productions. There is no such thing as a stress-free buildup, however, with so many balls in the air. The goal was to minimize the hand-wringing and grinding of teeth as much as possible.

The next stress point was Susan's wedding invitations. Annie had designed them, but when they arrived, Susan didn't like the font Annie had chosen at all. Annie called me at work to inform me of the crisis.

"Susan hates her wedding invitations," she informed me.

"Tell her to get new ones so she's happy," I responded. "You now have some expensive paper you can use for notes. Case closed."

I said that as much for Annie as for Susan. I don't like wasting $600 any more than the next person, but my thought was to not sweat the little things. In the old days, Annie never would have called me about something like that. She would have just handled it herself, and probably would have told Susan to just put up with it. Thankfully, we didn't have any other problems of note after that.

Oh wait, there was one other small problem from which I learned to keep my mouth shut after making one complaint. With three weddings and three rehearsal dinners, Annie wanted to wear a different dress to each event.

"You can wear the same dress for all the weddings, can't you?" I asked quite naively.

"No, I can't!"

"You can at least wear the same thing for the rehearsal dinners."

"No, I can't!"

So she got six new outfits, three for the rehearsals and three for the weddings. I wanted this to be a highlight year for Annie to the extent that I caved on the issue of her dresses.

The Lulloff family looking our best for Susan's wedding on June 7, 1997. From left, Andy, Susan, Rolf, Annie, and Sarah.

What was I thinking?

I figured I had to do something special for Annie in celebration of these weddings. But what? I've got it. I'll buy her a charm bracelet, and I'll have the first charm be our wedding date. And then as each of our kids' weddings takes place, I'll give her an additional charm with that date. I was already giving myself a spousal gold star for coming up with this idea.

We got home late after the first wedding, which was Sarah's, and Annie quickly drew a bath. She was in the tub when I walked into the bathroom with a blue, wrapped box from Bake's Jewelry. She knew a blue box meant Bake's.

"What's that?" she asked, obviously intrigued.

"Just a little something for you," I said.

"Can I open it now?"

"You bet. I'll be happy to watch you open it."

It contained a charm with that day's date. I'm convinced that made her love me even more, and I enjoyed presenting her with a new charm after each of the weddings.

***

Going to weddings certainly beats the heck out of going to funerals, and we attended as many weddings as possible. By my count, we went to more than fifty weddings during the years we dealt with Parkinson's. The socialization aspect of these events is very helpful for both the care person and the care partner, and it provides some motivation to work on your mobility, balance, and strength. The more you can interact and live a fulfilling life rather than retreating into the darkness of isolation, the better.

Annie and I were planning to attend a Sunday wedding in a Washington, D.C., suburb for our friends' son in August of 2000. We made arrangements to fly out at 4 p.m. that Saturday, meaning I had plenty of time to participate in a golf outing that morning at Oneida. Our club professional met me when I returned to the clubhouse after the event.

"Call your wife right away," he said. "She is fit to be tied and has to talk to you now."

This was before personal cellphones were common, so I made the call from a phone in the pro shop.

"What's wrong, Annie?" I asked. "Jim told me I needed to call you right away."

"We're not going to the wedding. I've got a terrible mess here!" Annie replied, sounding quite angry. "The goddamn washing machine leaked, and water is running down into the basement! My clothes are soiled and we can't go."

I drove home immediately and arrived to a complete mess, as Annie had described. She was distraught.

"There is no way we can go," she informed me.

"I'll take the clothes to the laundromat and we'll be okay," I said, trying my best to calm her down.

When I returned a little while later, clean clothes in hand, I could hear "bang, bang, bang" as I got out of the car. I went inside and found Annie in the laundry room. She had a sledgehammer and was punishing that poor washing machine for its misdeeds.

"That goddamn machine is never going to work again," she said. "I'm going to make sure of that!"

We made our flight on time, and of course by the next day Annie was feeling much better. We had a wonderful time at the wedding. She was still vibrant at this time, and obviously her energy level could elevate when emotion kicked in. Looking back, it was actually kind of funny. I learned from this experience that Annie was always right, I needed to keep her happy, and never have a sledgehammer within her reach.

Mobility becomes a bigger challenge

Mobility issues are totally dependent on the situation. For example, the Paris airport was not user-friendly for people with disabilities when we were getting ready to fly back from France on one of our last European trips. The customs area was jammed with people and there were no chairs. I thought this was ludicrous.

"Annie, are you okay?" I asked.

"Yeah," she replied, but I could tell she was not.

"The next time we travel, we're going to take a travel chair with us," I said.

"Okay," she said.

Annie understood her increasing limitations and generally was cooperative.

The same mobility concerns became apparent when we flew to Florida to spend time in our condo. We bought the condo in 1996 and were good for about ten years before her first back operation required a heightened attention to care. We would have her in the travel chair getting on and off the plane. It was very convenient, because the airline would check the chair at the door and have it waiting for us as soon as we stepped out upon arrival. We also began using the travel chair when going to events at Oneida Country Club. It is a long walk from the front door to the dining room, and using a walker became more of a problem than a benefit from a functional standpoint. The walker caused her to lean forward and shuffle her steps, which was not safe.

Our safety concerns initially focused more on her back, but then her Parkinson's mobility gradually became the greater concern. By that time, her cognitive impairment helped the situation. Be it from increased apathy or cognitive impairment or a combination, Annie didn't realize how limited she was and just accepted our suggestions. We didn't make an issue of it, so neither did she.

The travel wheelchair we took with us when we traveled through airports toward the end of her journey didn't guarantee complete safety, however. One day in 2013 at the airport in Fort Myers, Florida, I turned her chair around to back her over a bump only to have the wheels suddenly catch on a crack in the sidewalk. Boom! The chair flipped and threw Annie onto her back. A crowd gathered immediately and offered to get first aid. She was okay, thankfully. Looking back, I can see she had a gradual transition from accepting her disability to having apathy toward it, and at the end being totally oblivious to it.

Annie was really struggling with her Parkinson's as well as some back pain in 2012. We had met a couple from Michigan when we were visiting Florence, Italy, in the spring of 2000. Dr. Larry Elmer was a neurologist, specializing in movement disorders, and chair of the neurology department at Medical College of Ohio, located at the University of Toledo. He asked if we were seeing a movement disorder subspecialist for Annie's Parkinson's disease. I said no and asked if he would recommend that we see such a specialist. He strongly recommended we add that to our care routine.

When we returned home, we made an appointment to see Dr. Karen Blindauer, a professor of neurology and Parkinson's specialist at the Medical Froedert College of Wisconsin in Milwaukee. She had trained in Dr. Elmer's program. We saw Karen twice a year for several years after that. We also spent a few days with Dr. Elmer in Toledo on our one and only drive to Florida. It was twelve years after we first met him in Italy.

Going out to eat became more of a challenge as Annie's mobility declined. We also had some of our best memories at restaurants across the country. For example, we would take our time driving to Kansas City to visit Susan and Monty and their sons. We would stop in Minneapolis first to visit members of Annie's family, and then continue south to Kansas City. Annie could tolerate being in the car for about six hundred miles per day, which is more than some completely healthy people can take.

The last time we made this trip by car, we stopped overnight in Dubuque, Iowa, on the way back to Wisconsin. It was a cold, fall night about five years before Annie's journey ended. The skies were spitting snowflakes as we decided to find a Friday night fish fry. I asked the manager at the little hotel we stayed at if he had any recommendations, and he suggested we try the Applebee's a mile down the road.

The parking lot was full, but thankfully there was one disabled parking spot left and I had a card to put in our window. We went inside and the place was jam-packed. The hostess was very nice and informed us a table just opened up and she would seat us right away. It was obvious that Annie was challenged, as I was holding onto her as we walked in.

When we had finished eating, our waitress left to get our bill. She never came back to our table, so I got the attention of another waitress and asked if she could find out what happened. She was gone for about five minutes as well. Finally, she returned and told us our bill had been taken care of.

"What do you mean?" I asked.

"The owner's policy allows us, one night per week, that if we see somebody who strikes us by how they act with each other, we can take care of their bill," she explained. "The two of you impressed us. The love, the concern that you two showed each other meant a lot to us employees."

We enjoyed a similar experience at an Outback Steakhouse in Appleton, Wisconsin. We were visiting my brother Kim and his wife, Jeannie. Kim was struggling with Alzheimer's disease and not at all steady on his feet. It was apparent that he and Annie both had disabilities. When we asked for the bill, the manager came to our table and said he had taken care of it.

"You guys have been here before," he said, "and we've always been impressed with the four of you. You deserve a treat tonight."

There are so many good people out there. We learned to be gracious and accept kindness from complete strangers as well as those close to us.

The 1990s come to a close

The vague symptoms and years of "undiagnosis" were so stressful, especially for Annie. But once we knew what was going on and got through the immediate sadness, we told each other we just had to deal with it.

The beginning of the decade of the 1990s, which coincided with Annie's official diagnosis, featured our kids all far away from home. This was a source of stress for Annie. We traveled out to Stanford at least twice a year, including family Thanksgiving celebrations. We flew the kids to where we were going to be, including dinner in a chateau at a Napa winery one year. It was great fun and a special time for our family.

These experiences were so nice. A special time stands out when Annie caught some type of a bug after eating at a Mexican restaurant on the Monterey Peninsula. She was the only one affected, but thankfully she was able to join us at Pebble Beach for Thanksgiving dinner the next day.

We visited Yosemite National Park for a few days when we went to California for Sarah's graduation from Stanford. Annie couldn't hike in the hills, but she could walk on the grounds and we stayed in the park lodge, often hanging out with Susan. Susan liked to walk, while Andy, Sarah, and I would go for runs. Annie loved to go shopping, and a clerk at Nordstrom's even sent a box of chocolates to our home.

Enjoying Vail, Colorado, in 1993 with our friends George and Sharon Hartmann (left).

I saw my role as keeping Annie happy. I wasn't a flower person, but I made a point of always giving her jewelry on special occasions. We had a wonderful, romantic life throughout our journey. It's interesting. I think about our sex life, and we were able to remain active through the 1990s. Going to our condo on Sanibel Island was like a honeymoon every time through about 2010. That was about the time things weren't going to work any longer, but we still hugged a lot. Of course, I wish we would have hugged even more.

Annie stayed physically active through much of the 1990s. She had substituted golf for tennis, and we were able to go on bike rides until about 2007. In fact, two years in a row we biked the Mountain Bay Trail on the Fourth of July from the edge of Green Bay all the way to the city of Pulaski, about fifteen miles each way. We stopped in Pulaski to have a burger and enjoyed the day together.

We rode bikes for about the first ten years of owning our Florida condo, often five to ten miles most days at a comfortable pace, and we would walk on the beach as well. Our bicycling came to an end one day in the late 2000s when we were riding to Bailey's General Store on Sanibel Island, a relatively short distance from our condo. I rode behind Annie so I could keep an eye on her balance.

We were riding on a paved pathway, with brush and swampy areas along the sides. Suddenly, she started to slow down. She might have passed out. Her wheels turned to the right and she crashed into the brush before I could react. She was not hurt and I was able to help her up so we could make it back to our condo. Thankfully, we were close to home, but that was the last bike ride she ever took.

We had an exercise bike in our basement in Green Bay, and that worked okay for a few years until her balance issues made that unsafe as well. After that, we purchased a NuStep recumbent exercise machine. It enabled us to get Annie the aerobic exercise stimulation that is important for most people, and I still have it in our house today.

Exercise as part of your treatment

Walking, jogging, bicycling, or using an exercise machine can make up for the limitations of poor balance when done safely. The positive stimulation you enjoy from the many invigorating aspects of exercise helps the neurons in your brain work better. Some of that stimulation is physical, but there is an emotional benefit to exercise as well. It has been shown to help with depression and anxiety, and interacting with other people during exercise can deliver an added boost.

Our brain produces a molecule called BDNF (brain-derived neurotrophic factor) as a result of exercise that plays an important role in brain health, especially as it relates to learning and memory. When I run, it helps me deal with the stresses in my life. For Annie, I noticed that it improved her mood.

We put our NuStep machine on our back porch rather than in the basement for two reasons. First, exercising outside, or at least in natural light, stimulates the mind more than is possible in a basement. Second, it was becoming too risky to have Annie safely navigate the staircase to get down to the basement.

The NuStep machine includes a swivel chair, side rails, and straps for your feet so you don't slide off the pedals. You can adjust the seat and the level of resistance, and you can work your arms and legs during your workout. It is difficult for people with Parkinson's to get aerobic exercise. Walking is fine, but it doesn't get your heart rate up. We also couldn't use a treadmill because Annie would fall in the first second. Plus, it was a challenge just getting her to the basement to use it. Again, live and learn.

The NuStep turned out to be an ideal solution for us. I got Annie on the machine one day on the back porch, and she was cranking along nicely, watching TV in the process.

"I'm impressed," I said. "You haven't been on the NuStep for two weeks and it's as though you haven't missed a beat."

She continued at a strong clip for about twenty minutes before she was ready to stop. The readout said the resistance level was at a seven out of ten.

"Wow," she said. "I didn't think it was that high."

I got on the machine to confirm the reading, and I can tell you it took some work even for me to go at her pace. That was really encouraging for both of us.

Any kind of exercise always needs to keep safety in mind. Falling is never allowed. What worked for you a year ago may not work now. We had been able to ride our bikes together in Florida, but that had to end once Annie's mobility challenges and fluctuating blood pressure made that too dangerous. That decision took away some of her independence, but the benefit of keeping her safe was worth it.

"I'm your insurance policy," I said. "If you start to fall, I can't catch you fast enough to ensure you won't get hurt. The next fall might be fatal, and we don't want that to happen."

I had to take charge of the situation because Annie no longer could make good decisions with regard to her capabilities.

The Sally Ann advantage

There came a point in our journey when it became evident Annie should not be left alone. The key was to find someone Annie accepted, and not everyone who came into our home was a good fit. Sally Ann Schuyler quickly became that person for us. She and Annie bonded, and her presence was a huge help as I transitioned to part-time work in 2012 when I turned seventy.

The addition of Sally Ann to our in-home care team for the last ten years of our journey provided a great comfort level for me. Her presence gave me the flexibility to do errands, go out for a run, and play golf on Thursdays. She assisted with general care, and there were even times she was able to care for Annie while I dealt with my own health issues. Not everything that happens in life follows a convenient schedule, and that includes the health of the care partner.

One snowy February morning in 2019, about two years before Annie's passing, I woke up with stomach discomfort. We had received about a foot of snow the night before, and I went outside to shovel off the cover of our hot tub so it wouldn't collapse under the weight. I was nauseated and wondered if I had the same severe stomach virus I had a few months earlier. The norovirus outbreak in 2018 produced violent vomiting and diarrhea, and it hit me hard.

When Sally Ann arrived shortly after I was finished shoveling outside, she took one look at me and asked what was wrong. I had grabbed a bucket and told her I thought I might have the flu again as she focused her attention on Annie. All of a sudden, I had to rush into the bathroom. I was having dry heaves and a normal bowel movement. That was better than the last time I was sick, I thought, because I had diarrhea so badly then. But my stomach still hurt this time and it kept getting worse. I self-diagnosed that my small intestine likely was twisted, which causes a lack of blood circulation to a particular area of the intestines. The pain can be intense.

I called Sarah, who is a physician, and she immediately ordered me to the emergency room. I called a neighbor to drive me to St. Vincent Hospital, where my friend Dr. Peter Falk was on call. He took me into surgery and found that my small intestine had twisted on some scar tissue from an appendectomy I had when I was eighteen years old. He removed two feet of my small intestine and I was in the hospital for six days. It was not much fun.

It was a rude awakening to the real world of providing Annie with seamless care. She was not used to me being gone for so long, and her understanding of the situation wasn't always very sharp. Even after returning home, I was under strict orders not to exert myself, and that included not helping Annie out of bed. We enlisted a team of care partners to help with Annie during my recovery and look out for me. Susan came up from Kansas City and spent a week with us, Sarah pitched in when she was available, and we had an outside agency provide some in-home assistance as well. Some of these people were more highly skilled than others.

I was able to take over as Annie's primary care partner again after about three weeks, but it certainly was a reminder that life can be unpredictable. Things don't always go smoothly with the care partner's health, either. Thank goodness Sally Ann was able to help as much as she did.

I'll let Sally Ann describe her experience with us for the final decade of Annie's life:

"Annie was still trying to walk when I first began helping with her care. She had broken her hip at that point and was recovering from that, but she was still thinking she could do a lot of things by herself. Rolf told me she could have absolutely no more falls.

"Annie wanted to weed the flower beds at one point. They were weedy because Rolf was still working. She would sit on the lawn and weed the flower beds for an hour or so. Then we would sit on the deck under an umbrella and have a peanut butter and jelly sandwich.

"She had some cognitive challenges, but she could still do some things. I would be there to catch her if she started to fall and slowly lower her to the floor. She would sit there and laugh and then say, 'Dammit, I guess I can't do that.' Not being able to do laundry was a hard thing for her to accept. She started going downhill and wasn't able to stand anymore. I would pick her up and pivot her onto the wheelchair or the toilet. Whenever I would tell her that something wasn't safe for her anymore, she would say, 'Is that according to the boss?' or 'I suppose the boss said that,' meaning Rolf. She would accept that, and it got easier toward the end as she would fall asleep and forget about it.

"Annie loved taking hot baths when I started, but the last couple of years that wasn't safe anymore. Rolf and I discussed it, and he decided that we would give her a shower together. Rolf put on his swimming suit and got in the shower with her. All along, I tried to help her with her independence to make sure she didn't feel like I was taking everything away from her. She still wanted to make choices for herself. If she didn't want to do something, we just didn't do it.

"I would like to think Rolf and I had a good care partnership. Rolf and Annie were an inspiration to me as individuals and as a couple. They were always so family-oriented. Whenever I think I'm maybe having a bad day, I'll just think of Annie all those years struggling with that disease. Everyone treated me so kindly. In all my years of caregiving, I have never been blessed with such a wonderful family. It was an honor and a privilege to be trusted with their loved one's care."

Sally Ann, we were blessed to have you on that journey with us. I don't know what we would have done without you.

***

We were also blessed to have several friends, family members, and assorted angels who helped Annie and me during our journey. Libbie Miller was a wonderful addition to our care team. Libbie was in her late-eighties and lived by herself next door to Sally Ann, but the two women did not know each other well.

I met Libbie our first year in Green Bay. She was a physical therapist, and to this day she was the best I've ever had the honor of working with. She came to the Midwest from New York and completed her physical therapy (PT) training at Mayo Clinic in Rochester, Minnesota, during the time when polio was still a prominent disease. The PTs back then didn't have magic pills. They had iron lungs that supplied the breathing for many of the people who couldn't breathe due to the paralysis that polio sometimes caused. They were true hands-on scientists.

Shortly after we arrived in Green Bay in 1974, I occasionally would see students from Syble Hopp School, which is a county-funded school that provides an educational setting and program options for children and young adults with intellectual and other developmental disabilities. Libbie worked at Syble Hopp and I first encountered her there. She was such a joy to work with because she was so good.

About five years before Annie passed away, I was at a grocery store on Christmas Eve when I came around a corner and saw Libbie.

"Hello, Rolf!" she said.

"Hi Libbie!" I replied. "Merry Christmas … I mean, Happy Hanukka!"

"It's the same God," Libbie reassured me with a smile. "How's Ann?"

"We're challenged," I admitted, "but we're hanging in there."

"I'm going to a continuing education program in Milwaukee the second weekend in January," she said. "It's about using music therapy and physical therapy to help people with Parkinson's disease. After I come back from that course, could I come over and see Ann?"

"That would be wonderful," I said.

"I could come over once a week," she offered.

"That would be great," I said, "but I am going to pay you."

"Then I'm not coming," she replied, putting an end to the negotiation.

Libbie did indeed start coming to the house, and for the next two years she came virtually every week for an hour or more.

Libbie and Annie really bonded. She would help Annie walk out onto the back porch, where they would sit face to face and do exercises while music played. I could hear them laughing, talking about gossip, and generally enjoying their joyful relationship.

One day, I noticed Libbie limping slightly during her visit. She already had had both of her hips replaced.

"You're limping a little bit, Libbie," I mentioned.

"No, not really," she replied.

"You should see your doctor for that," I pressed.

"He says it's okay," she stated.

At that, I kept my mouth shut and helped her out the front door on a beautiful May morning. I was loosely holding onto her arm.

"You don't have to hold me," she insisted, and pushed my arm away.

She took two steps down to our front sidewalk and crumpled to the ground on the brick pavement. I could hear a loud crack of a bone snapping.

"I just broke my femur," she said, looking up at me.

"I heard it," I said.

"I heard it, too," added Sally Ann.

"It broke before I fell," Libbie informed us.

She went on to have surgery and recovered quite well, which didn't surprise me knowing her grit and toughness. As of this writing, Libbie is still a wonderful, dynamic person. She volunteers at the Aging & Disability Resource Center, leading exercise programs for older women, many of whom, like her, are in their nineties. She is salt of the earth and was so therapeutic for Annie.

Sally Ann and Libbie are golden examples of some of the wonderful people who impacted our lives. I believe one of the reasons these women connected so well with Annie was this is the type of person she was as well.

Green Bay is a giving community in which so many people do so much good for others. She discovered this early on because many of the people she met through tennis were involved in community groups and they introduced her to the good causes with which they were involved. Along with her PEO group, Annie also became involved with the Service League of Green Bay, Howe School and the Howe Community Resource Center, and she and I served on our Union Congregational Church's board of deacons and deaconesses for four years.

Loss of femininity

Loss of femininity had a quiet, yet tremendous impact on Annie's attitude. She was depressed and anxious already, and now she had to deal with losing her feminine pride due to issues with bladder control. This is not unusual for Parkinson's patients as overall muscle control becomes more and more of an issue. A lot of people who don't have Parkinson's develop urinary incontinence, too, but that doesn't make it any easier to accept.

This happened gradually for Annie, beginning with having to go to the bathroom every hour. She frequently didn't make it in time. She would wet her clothes and had to start wearing Depend underwear. She hated that. She felt like she was no longer a clean lady. All of a sudden, she viewed herself as an old lady with wet pants. I couldn't blame her for feeling depressed about it.

We tried a variety of medications to stop the progression. Annie saw several doctors including a urologist, her OB-GYN, and a neurologist. It turned out the side effects of the pills they gave her created bigger problems than the bladder control.

"I can't stand taking these pills," she said. "I feel weird and I don't know what's going on."

Her Parkinson's medications often did not work as well when she had urinary tract infections. A UTI doesn't always present with symptoms. Oftentimes, we would not have realized she had an infection without being tipped off by the fact her medications were not working.

Varying levels of incontinence are common for most people as we age. Annie's issues dramatically increased later in her journey, which was not unexpected. That didn't make it any easier for her to accept, especially when we traveled and spent nights away from our own bed.

As Annie lost her ability to exercise on her own, we adopted a teamwork approach to ensure movement remained part of her life. Any and all types of movement are so important in maintaining safety and a good quality of life. My advice is to try different things, because you won't know right away what works and what doesn't. In fact, what worked yesterday may not work today or the other way around. Most days, Annie's motivation was pretty good. Others, not so much.

We would sit opposite each other in chairs and I would try to make a game out of it. I would put on some music to encourage her to move. We would practice leaning side to side, and backward and forward. The first time we did this exercise, I noticed she would barely move forward on her own. Her perception was that she was leaning forward much more than she actually was. So I took her by the hands and gently pulled her forward. We did that a few times, and then she started to do it on her own. We had awoken her ability to lean forward.

This was a great example of how quickly neuroplasticity can retrain the brain, either waking up the portion of the brain that controls that particular movement or engaging another part of the brain to override the diseased part of the Parkinson's brain.

The same dynamic happened with Annie's walking gait. Her stride length had gradually shrunk to very short steps, so we needed to override the part of her brain that was telling her to slump forward and shuffle her steps. We started to work on that regularly. Progress was inconsistent at first. She would take a normal-length step, but then quickly revert to taking little steps again.

I began instructing her to stop the second she started to shuffle. My thought was we couldn't allow her Parkinson's brain to dictate her movement. After a month of consistent attention to her walking, Annie was able to walk the entire length of our house from the bedroom to the kitchen. We were even able to put away her walker most of the time.

Now, will techniques like these work for everyone? Maybe not, but you won't know until you try. It worked for this lovely lady for several years. We got her walking safely again, albeit with me at her side.

Brownies bring a smile

Annie loved brownies and could make a delicious batch. They always brought a smile to her face, but not always for the obvious reason. One year, a plate of brownies was at the center of a humorous incident on our friend Sharon Hartmann's birthday.

"Happy birthday!" Annie said to Sharon over the phone. "I'm going to bring something over for you later today."

Annie had bought a little gift and drove over to the Hartmann home. However, by the time she arrived, Sharon must have left on an errand and there was no answer at the door. There was a plate of brownies on the front porch, which Annie assumed Sharon had left for her. So she left the present on the porch and took the plate of brownies with her, eating one on the way home.

Half an hour later, Sharon called to thank Annie for the present.

"Sharon, let me ask you a question," Annie said. "Did you put a plate of brownies out on the step for me?"

"No, someone else was going to drop off a plate for me," Sharon replied.

"I'll be right over with that plate, but it will be shy one brownie," said an embarrassed Annie.

That story went viral with her friends and she never lived it down.

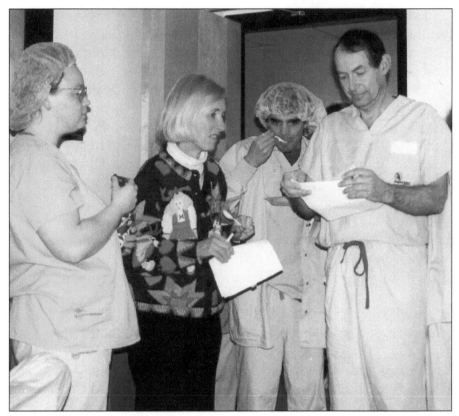

Annie and I were two of the judges for the annual brownie contests we had with the operating room team at St. Mary's Hospital Medical Center. This picture is from the first one in 1995.

Brownies also were a popular topic among the operating room team at the hospital. I knew I had to get Annie involved in this somehow.

"Annie, the kids in the OR want to have a brownie contest, and they would like us to be the judges," I said.

She was more than happy to help out with such a grueling task. Along with one of the anesthesiologists, we graded twenty plates of brownies identified by codes so we didn't know who made them. Annie served as a brownie contest judge for four years in the late 1990s and loved every bite.

One last backhand

We visited Susan and her family in Kansas City in October 2019, less than two years before Annie passed. She was really struggling by this point and we were staying at a hotel rather than at Susan and Monty's house. We went over to Susan's house the afternoon we arrived, and her younger son, Carter, said, "Grandpa, let's go downstairs and play ping pong."

I told Annie what Carter and I were going to do, and she said, "I'll come and play, too."

Everyone's mouths dropped open in shock.

"Good idea!" I said.

We slowly walked her down the narrow stairway to the ping pong room. I stood her up at the table, steadied her with my hands on her hips, and gave her a paddle. Carter hit an easy ball and Annie's return attempt went into the net. The next time, they were able to volley a few times.

Then I could see Carter get a smirk on his face and he hit the next ball hard to Annie's backhand. Only she returned it in the blink of an eye!

"Great shot, Gramma!" Carter said. "Your tennis genes are coming out."

It was a special moment for all of us. The fact we live so far away from each other was difficult for Susan, and this touching interaction was something none of us will forget. Here are her thoughts on the subject:

Annie surprised us with her ability to return a hard shot at the ping pong table from our grandson, Carter (off camera to the right), as his brother, Connor, watched.

"My kids got to know their grandma, although one of my boys said to me later, 'I wish I'd known Grandma Annie before she had Parkinson's.' By the time they were old enough to really know her, she had a hard time walking. My dad would run out in the backyard and throw a baseball with them. My mom's relationship with them was different, but she found things that she could to do to bond with them. One of her favorite things to do was read to them.

"I wish there was a way I could feel how she felt even for a day; to really understand how she felt. You could see the frustration at times. She wanted to do the things she wanted to do. Shopping was a huge thing during visits, but gradually we had to scale back on the amount of shopping we did. She just wanted to keep on going.

"Now that I'm a parent, I realize she made her job look easy and just got it done. I never heard her complain about not feeling well. I didn't see the worry that had to have been part of her daily life. Life was simpler then, but she made it look easy. The laundry was always done; the house was always clean. She even took care of all the car maintenance, and if anything needed to be fixed in the house, she did it. Our parents were just a good team."

Chapter 5

Falling Is Never Allowed

Fall prevention is absolutely critical when it comes to living with Parkinson's disease and caring for your partner. Nothing can derail your efforts faster and with more lasting consequences than a fall. Whether you think balance issues are currently in play or not, I cannot stress enough the wisdom of swallowing your pride and erring on the side of safety. This includes using aids such as walkers and wheelchairs, taking elevators instead of stairs, and accepting a ride from an airport passenger assistance vehicle.

It is so much better to be safe than sorry. Oftentimes the hardest part is using a walking aid for the first time, especially in public. We are all stubborn to some extent, and people with Parkinson's disease often are not fully aware of their limitations, refuse to acknowledge they exist, or simply downplay their severity. It is the responsibility of the care partner to encourage an attitude of safety first, as difficult as that might be. I know from personal experience that it can be extremely difficult to say no to your loved one.

Annie had three major falls in 2010 as she was dealing with advancing Parkinson's symptoms and the tail end of her back surgeries. She didn't seem to have major balance challenges, but she obviously did. Her falls may have been a contributing factor to the failure of rods in her back. Fatigue fractures in these rods arise from issues similar to that of bending a coat hanger. The more you bend it, the more heat it creates and weakens the metal. Eventually, this overloads the metal with stress and causes metal fatigue failure.

Her first fall occurred in March 2010 as she was entering the bathroom. I was watching her pass through the doorway when she suddenly lost her balance and fell onto a nearby armchair. All of the force of Annie's fall went directly onto her right ribs as she hit that armrest. I sprang up to help, but of course could not get there in time to prevent the fall. She was in a lot of pain, and a quick check suggested that she may have broken some ribs. Because of the amount of pain she was feeling and its location, I had two additional concerns. First, the liver is right underneath where she was having lower chest pain; and second, broken ribs potentially can puncture the lung and create air leakage. I had personally experienced a rib fracture as a result of a skiing accident. I didn't have any trouble breathing, but the area of the injury was really tender, and it hurt for a couple of months if I rolled over on it in bed.

It was obvious we needed to get Annie to the emergency room and have her checked out right away. X-rays and a CT scan confirmed she had fractured three ribs. Thankfully, the images did not show any evidence of damage to her lungs or liver. There really is nothing you can do to treat broken ribs other than rest and protect the injured area. Thankfully, she did not appear to have suffered any other internal injuries.

***

It is not uncommon for people with Parkinson's disease to lose their bearings like Annie did as a result of passing through a doorway or some other minor change in footing or surroundings. Going around a corner, starting or stopping suddenly, navigating even slight inclines or declines, transitioning between different surfaces such as concrete and grass or different types of carpeting can affect the brain's ability to maintain equilibrium. Part of falls prevention is being aware this can happen and paying attention to potential hazards. Training your brain

Enjoying popsicles in our kitchen with all the grandkids on July 16, 2010. (From left) Zita, Heidi, Claudia, Greta (in back), Ingrid, Wally, Carter, and Connor.

(leveraging its neuroplasticity abilities) to successfully adjust to these seemingly minor hurdles as they crop up is a key ingredient to falls prevention.

For us, going out on the back patio required a heightened level of caution. You don't have to have Parkinson's disease to be distracted when stepping over a hose or debris from a tree, seeing a squirrel run across the yard, or glancing at the pool. Carrying something as simple as a cup of water can be a risk factor as well. I caution visitors to be careful every time we go outside at our home.

Waiting too long to go to the bathroom also can create stress, rushed movements, and the potential for a fall. You are at increased risk when your bladder is bursting and you are hurrying. Annie and I discovered this at an airport on one of our trips. It wasn't just her bladder that she needed to empty, which made things even more urgent. I got her situated on her travel chair and she said, "Hurry!"

We got to the bathroom areas, only to find that the ladies room was out of order for cleaning. We didn't have time to continue down the concourse to the next ladies room, so I took her immediately into the nearby men's room. We were able to take care of her urgency in time, thankfully.

Poor muscle strength, visual problems, and balance issues all increase your risk of falling. We are all human and have varying levels of fitness. As a care partner, you must be aware of your own capabilities and limitations so you can provide the safest level of care for your care person. There is a pride aspect to avoiding falls in that we need to admit when age is causing our physical capabilities to decline.

Make sure you have handrails on both sides of all staircases, in the shower, and alongside the toilets. The care partner will have to compensate for their care person's increasing inability to be aware of potential fall risks. Exercise appropriately to maintain the strength you need to get into and out of chairs and your bed, walk safely, traverse stairs safely, and lift items and people as necessary. I helped Annie exercise regularly almost until the end of her life, and I am convinced that helped extend her quality of life.

Be proactive and do not wait for something bad to happen. The old saying that an ounce of prevention is worth a pound of cure has never been more accurate than with Parkinson's disease. Not only can a fall cause major injury, it will produce a significant setback for your care person's Parkinson's. The recovery period usually will be much longer that it would be for an otherwise healthy person, and the individual may never return to the state they were before the fall.

***

Annie's next fall three months later was extremely traumatic for me as the care partner, especially since I was right next to her when it happened. This was a good example of how quickly things can happen and that you cannot go halfway when it comes to safety precautions.

It was a beautiful Saturday morning in June as Annie and I slowly made our way down the driveway to look at some flowers in the yard. I was on her left, loosely holding onto her left arm. Her walking gait had shortened considerably by this time and her stride wasn't much more than a shuffle. She tripped on a small crack in the driveway and immediately fell forward, her head hitting the concrete with a loud "Crack!"

The impact knocked Annie out cold. She lay prone, unconscious, with the right side of her face on the pavement. Her breathing, color and pulse were good, but she was unresponsive.

"Annie! Can you hear me?"

No response. This was her first head injury, and it was a bad one. I had been right at her side, even touching her arm, and still I could not react quickly enough to prevent this fall.

Ordinarily, there would always be a neighbor or two out and about, or walking past on the street. But on this particular morning, I could see no one. My cellphone was inside the house and I didn't dare leave Annie. I decided to monitor her breathing and head injury for the next couple of minutes, hoping beyond hope that a neighbor would appear.

"God, we need you now," I said, looking toward the sky.

Finally, I could wait no longer. I briefly left Annie's side and ran into the house to grab my phone so I could call 911. It took an estimated eight to ten minutes for Annie to start regaining consciousness.

"Annie, can you hear me?"

"Yeah," she said quietly.

"You fell. Don't move, but can you move your fingers a little bit?"

She could, thank goodness.

"Can you move your feet?"

She could.

I touched her neck gently, and she didn't seem to have any pain. That did not mean she absolutely escaped a neck injury. You can't take any chances with potential neck injuries or you may risk damaging the spinal cord.

"We need to get you to the hospital and get you checked out," I said. "Don't move."

I knew enough not to move her by myself and let the pros take care of Annie from there. Soon after the EMTs arrived, they applied a neck collar and gently rolled her onto a backboard for additional stability on the ride to the trauma center at St. Vincent Hospital. Further tests showed Annie suffered a skull fracture and there was a small bleed in her brain (called a subdural hematoma).

The trauma surgeon and a neurosurgeon examined her, and she stayed in the hospital's intensive care unit overnight for observation. A follow-up CT scan the next morning showed the bleeding had stopped. The doctors saw her again and said she was safe to go home with me. We were fortunate in that her only restriction was she couldn't drive for six months because of being rendered unconscious.

***

Now, you're probably thinking ... "Wait, she was still *driving*??"

Not often and not far, but yes, she had been. Believe me, I'm not happy to have to admit that. I should have been stronger and put my foot down long before this, since her reaction times and decision making certainly were not safe anymore. I even had concerns about her driving going back to the mid-1980s when she began having issues with double vision.

This brings up a point with regard to driving privileges and other life activities for which care persons want to retain their control. These types of skills, which previously had been second nature, are so difficult for people with neurodegenerative diseases such as Parkinson's and Alzheimer's to let go. Their Parkinson's brain makes it more difficult for them to recognize their own limitations. They see the world through their brain, which says they are okay and doing fine. They do not realize their brain function is impaired to the point of compromising the safety of themselves and others. They are not rational, and it takes a strong care partner or family member to withstand the fury that likely will follow such a decision.

Even before this fall, I had made an effort to let Annie see for herself that she was not safe to drive. I took her down the hill to the parking lots at the village soccer field complex. We got out of the car and I told her she could go ahead and get into the driver's seat. She needed help, of course.

"Annie, you can't even get in the car," I pointed out.

"I'll learn how to," she stated, as adamant as ever.

It was painful for me to have to stand up to her. It got to the point we just didn't talk about it. I couldn't make that rational decision for her because she could never accept it. Our kids wouldn't argue with her, either, other than to say she shouldn't drive.

"Yes, I can," Annie would tell them.

"No, Mom, you can't," they would respond.

Then Annie would change the subject, much like a child does when they don't like the answer they receive from a parent.

Annie drove herself down the hill to a local Zesty's restaurant one day, and then couldn't get back in the car. Somebody helped her and she was able to get home.

Our daughter, Sarah, eventually became involved in the driving situation. I'll let her tell the story:

> We asked all five of her doctors at the time to come together on this issue.
>
> "Our dad is the one who bears the wrath of Mom being frustrated with this," I told them. "We would greatly appreciate it if you all could make that decision and let her know she can't drive."

> *One of the doctors offered a driver's evaluation as a solution. I called the evaluator afterward and asked how it went, and he told me she passed.*
>
> *"What? My mother has zero reflexes! She cannot even turn her head. She can't safely back up. There's no way she can safely operate a motor vehicle!"*
>
> *"She was able to complete all the tasks I asked," he replied.*
>
> *I should have just taken the keys away from her. She was still able to walk and was so determined to do things. Shortly thereafter, she broke her hip and that was it. My dad knew she couldn't drive, but he was the one who had to listen to her."*

As we prepared for discharge from the hospital after her fall, I had the neurosurgeon on my side when the topic of driving came up. At least I thought that would be enough to get Annie past the thought of driving.

"Now, Ann," he said, "anytime you have a head injury like this, you can't drive a car for six months. You will have to get medical clearance, have a doctor evaluate you, before you can drive again."

"Okay," she said.

We got home and Annie almost immediately informed me, "In six months, I'll be driving again."

"Don't count on it," I replied.

In hindsight, I should have said something less challenging such as "Time will tell."

"You've got a medical license, so you'll be able to clear me," Annie protested.

"No, I can't. That would be breaking the law."

I felt like she hated me because I "took her driver's license away." She said that to me on a number of occasions. I tried to be firm and loving and rational, but logic does not work when Parkinson's is having its way with your loved one's brain. Dealing with cognitive decline is so stressful. We tend to think from the perspective of our brain's normal function rather than the care person's current state. They also become talented at putting on a show. And being demanding. And laying guilt trips on people. It is part of the journey for which care partners need to be prepared.

***

Annie and me at her surprise seventieth birthday party, September 3, 2010.

We had about a four-month period where things remained generally stable before the next major event threw us a curveball. Annie's
third and final fall of 2010 occurred on October 26, which also happens
to be our daughter Susan's birthday. Tuesday was my operating day at
the hospital, and I knew Annie had reached the point where it would
be prudent to have someone stay with her. A friend of ours did home
nursing care, and she had a couple of women who worked with her. I
had arranged for their first visit to occur that Thursday.

"Annie, please be careful while I'm gone today," I said. "Don't do
any laundry or anything like that."

"I won't," she assured me. "Don't worry about it. I'm okay."

Wouldn't you know it, Annie did in fact try to do some laundry
while I was at work, and her efforts came with disastrous results. She
took an awkward fall and couldn't get up. Fortunately, she was wearing
her push button emergency call device, and she was able to activate the
system. The service called me, but my phone was in my locker while I
was in the operating room. Sarah was next on the call list, and the service did get through to her. An ambulance brought Annie to St. Vincent
Hospital, and doctors there diagnosed her with a fractured hip.

Annie already had Parkinson's disease for at least thirty-five years at this point, and the last thing her brain needed was another challenge like this. What happens to someone age seventy who breaks their hip? Are they ever going to be as good as they were? This is a steep hill to climb for a senior in good health, much less someone challenged by a neurodegenerative disease.

To add insult to injury, her Parkinson's was getting worse. It takes a good six months after a major injury to return to your previous health state. But add in the Parkinson's and you now have a gradual downhill course to contend with in addition to the recovery. Her medications were not working as well and she had a consistent string of urinary tract infections (UTIs). The UTIs often occurred whenever she would tell me, "My medicine isn't working as well today."

The prevalence of UTIs in Parkinson's patients likely is associated with the autonomic dysfunction that also affects the body's ability to regulate blood pressure and other subconscious functions. I was aware of Annie's swings between high blood pressure (hypertension) and low blood pressure (hypotension), which is not uncommon with Parkinson's disease and similar brain disorders. However, I learned not to let the presence of a strong pulse fool me into thinking everything was okay if she was unresponsive.

I wasn't familiar with the term "supine hypertension," but I would get to understand it all too well. This refers to a condition that people with autonomic dysfunction have when their blood pressure becomes too high when they lay down, and then significantly drops when they sit upright. Conversely, postural hypotension refers to low blood pressure when gravity causes blood to collect in the legs and lower body, and does not supply adequate blood supply to the brain.

Even though Annie was at high risk to fall, we managed to prevent that from occurring for several years. We traveled extensively and watched our son, Andy, and our two sons-in-law compete in the Ironman Wisconsin triathlon in Madison three times. She was not in a wheelchair all the time, and the rest of the family pitched in to ensure her safety. Any falls from this point forward came as a result of her fainting, either from postural hypotension or supine hypertension.

It would be four and a half years before Annie would pass out and subsequently fall. We were in a Madison hotel room on April 28, 2015, and Annie was sitting in a chair. I turned my back for a moment to pack her suitcase, and before I knew it, I heard a loud "Crack!" She likely fainted as a result of postural hypotension, and the result was a head injury with another severe concussion. We transported her by ambulance to UW Hospitals, where they evaluated her and conducted a CT scan. It was her fourth major fall, only this time it likely was due to her passing out first. She was unconscious for a good ten minutes in three of those falls.

Annie would not have another fall for almost five years when in January 2020, she again likely passed out while sitting and suffered another concussion. We were getting ready to go out to dinner with friends and I was helping her get dressed. I walked as quickly as I could to get her slacks from the closet, and as I was coming back, I heard that sickening crack sound again. Annie was unconscious on the floor and again needed ambulance transport to the hospital. I believe that postural hypotension was again the cause.

***

After Annie had her third fall, I told her, "You are not going to fall again. I'm going to be with you or Sally Ann is going to be with you, but we simply can't have you falling."

Our experience showed the benefits of a three-step strategy whenever we faced a challenge such as falling:

#1 – Do not accept what's happening as the way things have to be.

#2 – Figure out what you can do to make a difference.

#3 – Take charge of the situation.

Annie had outpatient physical therapy for a while, but it seemed that the LSVT-BIG therapy they were using was not effective for her. It was not improving her function. They were all good therapists, don't get me wrong, but I could tell by watching that Annie needed a different type of therapy than they were providing.

For example, one day a therapist told Annie to use her walker and stand up straighter. But Annie's Parkinson's brain quickly took over and she returned to a slouched posture and short, shuffling steps. I saw this as reinforcing the diseased part of her brain. We needed to engage a part of her brain that was working well and use that to substitute for the part that was not working. I reasoned that the best way to do this was by removing the walker and forcing her brain to retrain itself. I had to be certain she did not fall, and that made it mandatory that I was right there to control her movements.

After we got back home following her therapy, I took the walker away and loosely held Annie by her left arm. We practiced standing tall and taking longer steps. We had to retrain her brain to do these actions.

This required that we do it as often as possible, beyond having an hour-long PT appointment three times a week. We had to apply this brain retraining consistently.

"Annie, tomorrow morning we're going to start training ourselves to get all the way from the bedroom to the kitchen table without falling," I said. "We're going to do this without using a walker and without shuffling like your Parkinson's brain wants you to do."

Whether she really understood what I was telling her, I can't say. But she did accept it. The side benefit was by attacking her walking deficiency, we were seeing benefits to some of the other deficits involving activities of daily living (ADLs).

There was a lot of psychology involved in working with Annie to educate, train, and motivate her. Praise, laughter, and love go a long way toward helping your care person stay engaged and motivated to make progress. I learned I would see better results if I phrased my guidance in the form of a positive statement rather than criticism. For example, I would say "We are going to work on going the distance from the bed to the kitchen table safely, but it might take a number of weeks to see it work. I really think you will be able to do it."

The first morning we tried the new strategy, I put my hand under her arm for safety and encouraged her to walk correctly. First of all, stand up as straight as possible.

"On the count of three, let's walk to the kitchen. Big step with the left foot, then big step with the right," I said.

"You don't have to hold me," Annie scolded me.

"I'm not holding you," I replied, taking a soft tone. "I'm your insurance policy to make sure you don't fall. If I feel you start to go, I can catch you. Now, stand up tall and let's go!"

Annie predictably shuffled her first steps. She took a big step with the left, then half a step with the right, and started to shuffle.

"Stop," I said. "Your Parkinson's brain wants to take control. It's like having a bad habit, and you're falling into the bad habit. It's not your fault. We're going to train your brain to take big steps and stand tall as we do it."

Within a month, we were walking the ninety feet to the kitchen table most days without stopping, and most days without shuffling. Every so often, she would start to shuffle. I would stop her immediately, reposition her, and encourage her to start again with big steps, standing tall.

Within three months, we were even walking around our block. I would carry a chair so Annie could sit if she was tired. Periodically, she would start to shuffle and we would stop, then restart without shuffling. She could make that walk without her walker and without shuffling.

If she was having a bad day or her condition was deteriorating, which it did gradually, we had to be safe. I would walk with her for short distances, ensuring there was a place for her to sit, and that would usually mean having her travel chair right there. Plus, the increasing problems she had with blood pressure instability put her at risk of passing out. You learn that lesson the hard way the first time you need a backup and don't have one. I would be prepared if Annie was going to pass out, but you don't want to get to that point. That may mean going for short walks at home. We would try to maintain her movements as much as she was capable of doing.

It got old just walking around our block, so we drove to the Fox River Trail to enjoy the natural beauty there. The benches on the trail in downtown De Pere and Green Bay were helpful because they were only fifty to one hundred yards apart. I had to anticipate whether Annie was going to be okay until the next bench, and one hundred yards got to be too far. I would have to quickly lay her down on the grass if it became evident she was about to pass out.

Preventing falls comes down to preparation, both in terms of limiting risk and learning what your care person's tendencies are. We were maximizing what Annie could do and it was often a moving target.

I learned not to depend on Annie being able to accurately tell me how she was feeling.

"Annie, you're going to pass out," I would say.

"No, I'm not," she would reply, shortly before passing out.

We got her to age eighty and a half before all the Lewy bodies in her damaged brain got to the point where all we could do was walk her from the bed to the couch in the family room. It was time to just keep her comfortable, and she was quietly accepting of that.

The reality is some people's brains will fail regardless of the effort put in to retraining and keeping them viable. Annie's brain gradually failed, dramatically so over the final weeks. As a care partner, it's difficult to separate yourself from a degree of guilt in feeling that you could have done more. If we had trained her brain to walk properly earlier, would we have been able to prevent any of her falls? Would it have made a difference?

We did what we could with the knowledge we had to work with. My hope with this book is that it will arm you with the knowledge you need to make a difference.

Chapter 6

Strategies for Care

One of my regrets when it comes to Annie's care was that I was slow to identify things that were going to be a problem until they actually were a problem. Doing physical as well as mental exercises are critical in postponing the types of debilitating symptoms common with later-stage Parkinson's disease. Strengthening exercises, balance exercises, and even very simple brain exercises late in the journey all can make a difference. We had to adapt to how we did things as her capabilities changed.

The tendency for people going through physical challenges is to crawl into a shell. However, our brains respond positively to exercise, so we did everything possible to stimulate Annie's brain. We found that by keeping her active, it helped her mentally, emotionally, and spiritually, as well as slowing down the Parkinson's that was impacting more of her brain.

We could usually find a way to make a challenging day better and maintain a positive attitude. After one particularly rough day, I snuggled up to her in bed, hugged her, and said, "I love you, Annie."

"I love you, too, Honey," she said.

It's been a crappy day, hasn't it?"

"It sure has," she responded.

I could sense how down her mood was. We were both so emotionally down. As a matter of fact, I was probably more down than she was.

"We are going to make tomorrow better, and all our future days better," I said, knowing I needed to say something more to lift our spirits.

I started reciting the Lord's Prayer, and she joined me. I had never prayed out loud before. We prayed together out loud every night the rest of our lives together, and we never had a bad day thereafter.

Although I had not been the most spiritual person, I am much more spiritual now than I've ever been. It is obviously comforting, but this simple routine also solidifies the good things Annie brought to my life. I don't ever want to let that go, because her determination and spirit had such a profound effect on me.

Taking care of your brain is a lifelong task, one that can help you prevent or at least postpone future problems from occurring. Believe me, you don't want to go through decades with a debilitating disease if you can at all help it. Make every victory count, regardless of how small it might seem in the moment.

Your roles as care partners for each other require that you learn your own tricks of the trade. Your kids and other family members can fill in from time to time, but it's often not the same dynamic as that shared by spouses. They will need to learn their own tricks of the trade and figure out what works best for them.

Here are some basic thoughts to keep in mind as you work together:

- If you can't delay the onset of a problem, then you want to minimize its severity.
- If you can't minimize its severity, then you want to slow down its progression.
- If you can't slow down its progression, then you want to make modifications so you can better deal with its challenges.
- If you can't make modifications, then you need to work on steps that can help you reverse a downward trend.
- If you can't reverse the trend, then you have to find ways to adapt to your new reality.

One of my favorite tricks of the trade was changing the topic, much like a parent does when dealing with a child. The art of distraction can be very effective with anyone going through an emotionally challenging time. Whenever a topic came up that would cause Annie to become upset or she would refuse to talk about it, I would simply turn the agenda to something more positive. Our condo was a classic example of how a pleasant distraction could work wonders on her mood. It was like a toy for Annie, beginning with the trip she took on her own to pick out furnishings.

We shared a special experience there on November 23, 2002. We had arrived there that day to spend time over the Thanksgiving holiday. It was just the two of us. We were having dinner and turned the television on, and the news report noted that the space shuttle Endeavour was scheduled to blast off from the Kennedy Space Center, about 150 miles away. We went up to the rooftop of our condo to see if we could catch a glimpse from that distance, but NASA scrubbed the launch. We went up to the roof again the following night, and it appeared we were in for a repeat cancellation.

Annie turned to head back toward the staircase and go inside. She was okay using the stairs at that point, but we made sure to have people in front of and behind her the last couple of years we owned the condo.

At that moment, I saw a flare of light over the trees and a slow-moving fireball quietly made its way upward.

"Don't go!" I said before she could start downstairs.

She came back over by me and together we took in this spectacular event. We hugged and cried as we watched the shuttle's exhaust tail become longer with each second, soon separating into two flares as the boosters broke free and the main stage took over. It was just amazing.

Working together as care partners

Annie and I were fortunate in that we worked well as a team, but that becomes more of a challenge the farther you progress in your journey. How do you effectively deal with someone who won't agree to do the things you know they have to do? Or stop doing the things you know they shouldn't do anymore?

As the care partner, sometimes you just have to go with the flow when your care person does or says things that don't make sense. Remember that your biggest advantage in the battle against neurodegenerative disease is that you have each other. Hug each other and work to build that special rapport you had when you were young and madly in

Sarah, Susan, and Andy with us at our fiftieth anniversary family dinner, July 2014.

love. Is the fire as strong now as it was then? Likely not, but you can add oxygen to that fire and relight the flame.

You can't allow anger and frustration to control the situation. It creates animosity between you and a lack of trust for you as the care partner. It makes it easier to realize when to pick your battles when you are able to focus on understanding what's going on with a situation, and indeed, what's going on in their brain. For example, I learned not to argue with Annie when her Parkinson's brain told her that her mother was still alive and living with us. Just let it go, I told myself. Annie couldn't help it if she became angry. I could.

Physical disability comes in a variety of forms, and as a team you have to be ready for anything. Educating yourself is a good first step. There is much more information readily available online today than when Annie and I began our journey. You will encounter problems that you won't know how to handle, and that's to be expected. Avoid shrugging your shoulders and saying, "Oh well, it is what it is." Instead, encourage each other with statements such as, "No, let's make a difference with this damn disease."

We began by breaking down the specific segments of disability into walking, fall prevention, sitting and standing, and even swallowing as the disease progressed. Teaching your care person to remain as independent as possible requires them to learn how to do these activities safely. Neuroplasticity is our first line of defense in minimizing the effects of physical disabilities caused by brain disorders or injuries.

Neuroplasticity is the ability of our brains to develop new connections when the original connection no longer operates correctly. It is not just people dealing with neurodegenerative diseases such as Parkinson's who benefit from neuroplasticity. People with traumatic brain injuries (TBIs) suffered in accidents also need to retrain their brains in their recovery journeys. In fact, neuroplasticity is what happens in everyone's brain with regard to learning and skills development.

It also applies to those of us who are care partners when it comes to learning new skills. You may need to learn things you never dreamed would become part of your daily routine. That might include learning how to take your care person's blood pressure, for example. Learning new skills when you have a healthy brain is one thing; it's a whole other level of challenge if you have a Parkinson's brain. The rewiring process requires repetition and patience to relearn motions and activities that were second nature prior to the onset of the disease symptoms. If one strategy doesn't work, find something else that does.

For example, every time your care person sits down, have them stand up again right away. Do this three times. By the end of the day, they might perform this exercise twenty or thirty times. Breaking exercises like this into little sections throughout the day is much easier than doing them all at once, and there is a greater chance for cooperation if you do the exercises along with them. This is especially the case as apathy becomes more apparent during the Parkinson's journey.

I did chair exercises with Annie quite often. I would sit facing her so we could look each other in the eyes for a better connection.

"Okay, Annie," I would say. "Let's sit up tall. Now Annie, lean to the right. Lean to the left. Now lean forward."

The first day we did this exercise, Annie barely leaned forward at all. Her brain was telling her she was leaning forward, but the reality was she was not. Her brain had forgotten how to lean forward! I pulled her gently by the arms so her brain could feel the forward motion. This was an example of having to relearn a motion that she never had to cognitively even think about before. We needed to do this exercise repetitively to retrain her brain. Pretty soon, I didn't have to pull her forward at all. She was doing it on her own. The good news is relearning simple motions like this might not take long at all.

I would also have her sit with her arms outstretched and ask her to touch her nose with her fingertips. She wasn't close at first, but soon she was able to touch her nose regularly.

You can create your own occupational therapy exercises to help your care person maintain or regain what had been simple skills. Annie's gradual loss of control over her fine motor skills showed up in shaky handwriting and even using a spoon to put food in her mouth. We would use Cheerios to work on those skills. I would have her put a Cheerio on a spoon like she was going to put it in her mouth, only instead I would have her transfer it into an empty bowl we had nearby.

"This is stupid," she said at first.

"No, it's not," I said. "You have to reteach yourself how to do these things."

"This is like being a two-year-old. I don't need to do that."

"Yes, you do need to do it."

She may have complained at times, but usually she would become agreeable. When we lose skills that had been automatic, they are darn hard to gain back.

In addition to eating and drinking, a classic problem with Parkinson's is progressively speaking more softly. Part of the brain training I did with Annie involved the alphabet. We used it as a combination memory and vocal cord exercise. It even helped my memory.

"Now let's exercise your voice box," I encouraged her. "Let's shout out the alphabet. Ready? A!"

"A," she responded softly.

"Louder, Annie. A!"

"A," she said, this time a little louder.

I urged her to shout her responses louder and louder, and soon she was using her throat muscles to increase her volume significantly. Then we did it faster and faster. Her brain was waking up, in a manner of speaking, and her level of alertness increased.

By the end of the week, this became boring. It was time to change things up, so we started alternating letters. I would start with A, she would respond with B, and so on. We soon were able to do this very quickly, and it was fun.

"Now let's do the alphabet backward," I said with all the enthusiasm I could muster.

She gave me a look like I was crazy. The first time we tried it, I wasn't much better at going backward than she was. We started with just the final four letters: Z-Y-X-W. We repeated them a few times. Then we added a few more letters. We got to the point within a week or two that we could alternate letters going from Z to A almost as fast as we could go from A to Z.

I found that doing the alphabet backward was training my brain as well. By the end of the next week, we could go forward or backward, nonstop. It was a great brain exercise and allowed us to spend productive time together, strengthening our bond even further.

Doing exercises like this stimulates your life and enhances the level of socialization with somebody who is important to you. We emotionally tied ourselves together, which was exciting. As we get older, how often do we just accept the way we are instead of stimulating the excitement we used to have in our lives? Let's live with excitement now, too! In doing that, you find a way to turn boredom and routine into a special experience. Not only does it stimulate you, it fills you with understanding and love. It makes your relationship extra-special and generates a spiritual element to it all.

The interesting thing I learned from this exercise is the brain uses two mechanisms to complete this mental puzzle. One is rote memory, of course. But the other is I could picture the letters in my mind's eye. It was almost like I was reading the letters off a wall. We did the same thing with numbers, going up by three starting at the number one. We'd alternate between us; we'd change the numbers; we'd go forward and backward. It was stimulating her brain and encouraging neuroplasticity.

We would stand up after our chair exercises and I would put on a song by Neil Diamond. We would prance around together and hug. Annie was a great hugger, and that lives within me.

I still say to her, "Annie, I love you dearly. I still think of our first date, when we stood at your door and you said, 'Might I think that I'll be seeing you again?' When I said yes, you replied, 'I'd like that.' "

We embraced and hugged that night, and our love affair started right there on date number one. Recalling that night makes me love her more all the time. It's a great memory.

Maintaining a good quality of life

I find it easier to remember concepts when there is a pattern to the words that describe them. For example, as you might have noticed from the title to this book, I like words that begin with the letter 'L.' I have identified several 'L' words that you can keep in mind in striving to maintain a high quality of life. This holds true for both the care partner and the care person: Listen, Look, Learn, Like, Lead, Laugh, Love,

The grandkids were getting bigger by the time this photo was taken in July 2018. (From left) Andy and his wife, Elizabeth, Heidi, Carter, Zita, Ingrid, Wally, Greta, Claudia, Connor, Susan and her husband, Monty, and Sarah kneeling next to me.

Light, and Legacy.

Likewise, there are several words that begin with 'S' that I am convinced helped Annie live as long as she did:

Sustenance – Healthy nutrition is incredibly important because it provides the body and brain with the elemental tools they need to operate at a high level. It is easy for care persons to ignore their nutritional needs, especially as they decline. In fact, the stress of the journey can have this effect on care partners as well. Try not to let this happen for either of you.

Good nutrition is a pillar of brain health. Our brain needs fuel, because it uses a lot of energy. Being significantly overweight or underweight brings with it a host of what medical professionals refer to as co-morbidities. In other words, other things that can go wrong as a result of the main issue.

Too much sugar and too many simple carbohydrates are not good for us. Simple carbs are those that have had many of their nutrients removed. They spike your blood sugar, make you feel hungry quicker, and can contribute to unhealthy conditions such as type 2 diabetes and high blood pressure. White bread, enriched or refined pasta, pastries, and white rice are all examples of simple carbs. What's good for the body is good for the brain, and vice versa.

Know yourself and your family history, because we are all different. Each of us should fine-tune our dietary needs to our individual metabolic requirements. It is important to work with your healthcare providers to determine the appropriate dietary habits for you. Most healthcare organizations can give you access to good nutritional advice. However, experts generally agree that the Mediterranean diet and similar dietary programs are good choices for most of us.

Stimulation – Mental and physical stimulation are important for brain health. Scientific evidence shows that physical exercise (appropriate for the individual) clears the cobwebs out of our brain and helps us think more clearly. Physical exercise also helps with strength and balance.

Annie's stimulations over the years ranged from tennis to golf to social activities, bicycling, and walking. She even played the recorder instrument with a group of women for a while and performed community service with many organizations. Book club was a fun outlet for her. The group members would do table reads in which they would each take a role, and then they would discuss that section afterward.

In the early 1980s, Annie and some of her friends in the Service League of Green Bay performed a puppet show called *Count Me In*. The Green Bay School District was partners in the program. The play promoted awareness of the disabled, and the women traveled to elementary schools around the area to perform. Annie's hand-and-rod puppet, named "Sally," had cerebral palsy and used a wheelchair.

It was amazing how much Annie was able to accomplish during the early years of her Parkinson's journey, both before and after her official diagnosis. We had a full house of kids, and she always made sure there was a freshly cooked meal for our family dinners. We all sat down and ate together during those years. She also loved to dress up and look her best. Her attitude was somewhat of a throwback to an earlier time in that she was always dressed up when I came home from work. We kissed and hugged, and I appreciated that part of our daily routine greatly.

Music is a great brain stimulator. Safe dancing together, and singing along to your favorite songs and artists, activates the brain and strengthens your bond. Annie and I would use Neil Diamond as our go-to artist. We saw him perform three times in person, and we had a CD with twenty-three of his songs that kept us feeling good for as long as we let it play.

Our friend Libby Miller, a retired physical therapist, would also use music while spending time with Annie. She came to our house once per week for about two years, and the two of them hit it off great. They would move to the rhythm of the music while sitting in chairs.

Sleep – Getting a sufficient amount of sleep is critically important, especially for people with brain disorders such as Parkinson's disease. Disorders with REM (rapid eye movement) sleep can include thrashing and excessive body movement in bed. Thankfully, that never seemed to be a problem for Annie. She would make noise while breathing, but it was not due to obstructive breathing.

It is common for people in the final stages of life to sleep more often, eventually most of the time toward the very end. This was a blessing for Annie. It happened rapidly during her final week or so. My view was that if she couldn't be active, at least let her be comfortable. God saw to it that she slept away peacefully without pain or suffering.

Safety – Falling is never allowed, meaning you have to weigh the risks involved with certain activities versus the risk of falling. Stairs, or later on, even a slight change in carpeting thickness can become a fall waiting to happen if you aren't paying attention. While Annie was still able to use the stairs, we would make sure someone was on her down side to catch her just in case.

"Annie," I said in trying to inject a little humor into the situation, "this is the one time I get to put my hands on your cute little butt as you go up the stairs and not get in trouble."

Larger people certainly present a challenge that I did not have with my little Annie. If this is your situation, try to find a strong neighbor, friend, or family member who can assist with potentially dangerous movements and situations.

Safety must take priority over everything else, a concept that can be difficult to adhere to when it involves activities that your care person has enjoyed for many years. For example, Annie liked to swim in our pool, usually in water between three and four feet deep. I would stand outside the pool and watch as she swam across. We would talk for a minute, and then she would turn around and swim back.

"Annie, you ought to quit for today," I said one afternoon.

"No, I want to do it again," she replied.

She began slowly swimming again, but I noticed she was veering into a little deeper water. All of a sudden, she began sinking down into the water and her arms stopped. Fortunately, she was close to me and I was able to reach out and grab her arms to drag her out. The good news is she did not inhale any water, but she had passed out. It was about 2012, and that episode ended her swimming.

We also enjoyed our outdoor hot tub, although there was no doubt she was not safe there, either. We went in there once after she had to stop swimming, and I quickly realized there was no way we could do that. There was nothing she could grab onto. This was a typical sequence of events as we adapted to her evolving safe activity levels.

Socialization – To Annie's credit, she was never one to retreat into a shell. Sure, she had her battles with depression, but the surest way to pick up her spirits was a visit with friends or family. She absolutely loved visits from our grandchildren, and the two of us remained regular participants at social gatherings – both private and public – for most of her journey. Some of her friends would pick her up to go out to lunch during the last ten years of her life, and I soon began tagging along for safety purposes.

Even the exercises that she and I did inside our home were a form of socializing. We would touch each other's hands, mirror each other's movements, and often mix in a little dancing and hugging as part of the exercise regimen. I am convinced that social interactions kept Annie's brain active and functioning to the best of its limited ability much longer than it otherwise would have.

"Our mom made people feel comfortable," explains our daughter, Sarah. "She liked talking to people and it didn't matter what walk of life you came from. If you were a nice person and had something in common, she enjoyed your company and included you."

Annie always wanted to look presentable and loved getting her nails done, even as her condition continued to deteriorate. One day, the nail technician noticed Annie was wearing a nice bracelet and asked if it was new.

"Yes," Annie confirmed.

"Your husband certainly buys you nice jewelry, doesn't he," the woman asked rhetorically.

"Yes," Annie responded.

"You must be a really good lay," the woman stated.

"You'll have to ask Rolf, my husband," Annie replied with a twinkle in her eye.

That bracelet became known as "the good lay bracelet," and it showed she still had a sense of humor. I'm glad she said it.

Stress – You need to figure out who is going to be the best person to deal with this challenge. Some care persons handle it better than their spouses do. I had to make sure I wasn't the problem when it came to stress. It's easy to become the problem even though none of us do this intentionally. We are all different when it comes to our ability to handle different types of stress, whether that be health, financial, family issues, job issues, or all of the above.

You can't avoid the fact that life happens. Divorces and other issues within your extended family will happen, and tragic deaths, friends' cancer journeys, and countless other life hurdles inevitably will pop up. They did for us. In the end, the apathy that comes with Parkinson's dulled Annie's stress level. That made things a little easier for her, and I believe I was able to take away some of the stress burden from her as well.

"Don't worry, Annie," I would tell her. "The disease is the challenge, and we're going to fight it. We are going to make a difference."

Stress and anxiety are not the same as depression, although they can intertwine and make a person's mental health issues more severe. Some people very well may be suicidal. There are many resources available if you or your care partner are having suicidal thoughts. Please access them or call the Suicide and Crisis Lifeline at 988.

Stress is also a major mental health issue for care partners and the overall family support network. Share your stress with those around you. Don't hide it. People who struggle the most with stress almost always are those who try to hide it. Care partners need support just as much, and late in the journey even more than their care persons. Severe stress and depression are terrible things to live with.

I may be in denial, but I like to think I was able to stay pretty stable emotionally through Annie's journey. Now, did I have my crying episodes? Oh my God, did I ever. I immediately switched my focus to Annie and keeping her comfortable. Running helped reduce my stress level, there's no doubt about it. It cleared the cobwebs out of my brain and made my judgement better.

In retrospect, I probably didn't realize how much stress I was feeling. Sharing your stress journey often relieves stress for those who hear it. That's why I tell our story. I try to keep me out of it a little bit, but I realize I am part of Annie's story.

Swallowing – Maintaining or relearning swallowing skills is a huge issue when dealing with neurodegenerative diseases. The goal of safe swallowing is to hydrate, medicate, and nourish. Swallowing is an action we have known how to perform since we were infants, yet cog-

Annie got a big kick out of reading "Walter the Farting Dog" in December 2009, while Susan's boys, Carter (left) and Connor simply got a kick out of Gramma Annie.

nitive decline makes this an area of focus. It is separate from the autonomic dysfunction challenges that can impact blood pressure and heart rate. When parts of the brain no longer function properly, you have to do something to counteract it.

Swallowing can become a major issue for Parkinson's patients, and Annie was no exception. She began to have increasingly serious challenges with her swallowing skills the last eight years of her life, and it was something I was keenly aware of needing to monitor. In addition to the challenges her diseased brain presented, she also developed a physical issue that affected the mechanics of how she could open her mouth. Temporal mandibular joint pathology is a condition that causes the lower jaw to slide backward, even changing her facial appearance. This end-stage characteristic of Parkinson's amplified the challenges we had in getting Annie the nutrition she so desperately needed.

We had to wake up her mouth and her brain to prepare to swallow during the final stages of her life. I would have her open her mouth wide, stick out her tongue, and swipe it across her mouth from side to side, up and down. I would even have her shout a little bit, anything to get her alert. We would start by using a spoon with a little bit of water on it. It can be difficult to swallow pills even when you're not challenged with a brain disease, so you can imagine the hill we had to climb to get medicines safely down her throat by this point. I would grind them in

Celebrating my finish in the 2014 Boston Marathon in a Boston restaurant shortly before Annie experienced a significant choking episode.

a blender and add them to her smoothie. (More on smoothies shortly.)

We experienced a handful of severe choking episodes that resulted in trips to the emergency room or required fast actions. They were all very nerve-wracking episodes. She would get a little food stuck near her larynx where she couldn't get it to go up or down. It was right where you don't want it.

A major incident occurred in Boston after Andy, Sarah, and I completed the Boston Marathon in 2014. We had been in Boston for the marathon the previous year to cheer on Andy, which was the year of the terrorist bombing. We vowed to go back in 2014, and I obtained a waiver to run despite not having met the qualifying standard for my age. We took one of our surgical nurses along to care for Annie while we ran the race.

I was pleased to be able to run the entire 26.2-mile distance, finishing in 5 hours, 42 minutes at the age of seventy-two, which was good for me at that time. Afterward, our group went to a crowded German restaurant to get something to eat and rehydrate. We sat at a large table and I cut up some pieces of Wiener schnitzel for Annie. I didn't immediately notice, but at one point Annie struggled to swallow and had stopped breathing.

Andy's wife, Elizabeth, who is a nurse anesthetist, was the first to notice Annie was in trouble from her seat across the table. Elizabeth bolted out of her chair and flew around the table to a position behind Annie. She placed her hands underneath Annie's ribcage and pulled hard to perform the Heimlich maneuver. Nothing happened. Our friend Rob Moyer, an OB-GYN physician who had run the race and was eating with us, was next to try the Heimlich. This time, a chunk of food came out of Annie's mouth and flew across the table.

By this time, people throughout the restaurant had rushed to the scene. There were three doctors and an EMT at nearby tables, and the restaurant appropriately called 911. The ambulance arrived and the EMTs checked out Annie. Luckily, she was okay and there was no need to transport her to the hospital.

Another choking incident occurred during a dinner at Oneida Country Club. We already were at the point where we had to selectively choose what Annie could safely eat, and she was agreeable to that. Soups and other softer items were good, and she liked to go to Oneida. The members and staff were always very cordial, and they had been witnesses to our journey for many years.

We were having dinner in a small dining room on this occasion and had progressed to dessert. All of a sudden, I looked at Annie and recognized she was on the verge of having an obstructed airway.

"Annie, are you okay?" I asked.

She could only mumble in response.

I immediately laid her down on her side and performed a jaw thrust movement with my hands to correctly position her mouth. Elizabeth had taught me how to perform this technique. It elevates the jaw bone (mandible) and opens up the space in your throat. Another physician in the room came right over and asked if he should call 911.

"No, we've done this before," I assured him.

Annie responded well to jaw thrusts for airway control whenever she got something caught in her throat. You certainly do not want your care person to inhale anything into their lungs. These episodes can be terrifying, and we did have to go to the emergency room on more than one occasion.

The last time we had to go to the ER – other than after her final major fall – came during a luncheon at the Northland Hotel in downtown Green Bay on September 21, 2019. They were serving shrimp and beef, and the chef carving up the meat cut up some shrimp for Annie and me.

I had to go to the restroom at one point and asked another woman at our table to keep an eye on Annie while I was away. When I returned, I could tell something wasn't right.

"Annie, do you have some shrimp in your mouth?" I asked.

"Umm hmm," she struggled to reply.

I laid her on the floor, stuck my finger into her mouth and swept out the shrimp. By this time, many of the people in attendance had gathered around us. There was turmoil as people asked if they should call 911. If we had been at home, I would have just handled it. But I gave permission for someone to make the call and the ambulance took her to St. Vincent Hospital. They didn't do anything differently there, but better to be safe than sorry.

This type of episode heightened my fear of leaving her alone. Until you've experienced something like this, you don't know how you will deal with it. It's never easy. Annie's friends would take her out to lunch, and I would insist that she get only non-chewy foods such as soup.

We had a swallowing study completed as a result of these episodes. The speech therapist who did the evaluation said Annie should never use a straw to drink because she would be a risk to inhale, or aspirate, the liquid. However, I knew using a straw was also the best way to get her nourishment.

"Annie, we've got to get you swallowing better," I told her one day at home as I sat in a chair facing her. "Part of our swallowing is our tongue. Let's exercise our tongue, because it's a muscle."

Annie used to be able to touch her tongue to her nose, so I knew the dexterity of her tongue muscle had declined significantly.

"Let's open our mouths wide and sweep our tongue from one corner of our mouth to the other. That's good, now sweep across your upper lip," I said, demonstrating for her. "Now sweep across your lower lip. That good, now swallow."

We would do this several times per day, and the result was a dramatic decrease in the number of choking episodes for a while. We had ignored swallowing as a potential issue until we had trouble with it. By that time, we had missed our opportunity for taking preventive action. We may have been able to therapeutically do some things to slow her decline when it came to swallowing, but why not prevent it in the first place if possible, right? Working on neuroplasticity exercises for the throat helps the mood because it makes life fun again. Enjoying food and drink is part of our quality of life.

Smoothies delivered a calorie treat

Annie's inability to swallow well led to a steady decline in her weight to about ninety pounds near the end of her life. Her brain was no longer receiving adequate nourishment. I had to get some calories into her, so I decided to try spoon-feeding her with a little apple sauce. Once she proved she could handle that, I added her medicine to the mixture so she could get that down as well. Next, I had her drink a little water through a straw, and she passed that test, too.

She soon graduated to smoothies that I would make in the blender. There was not enough bulk in water to act as an effective stimulation for swallowing, while smoothies have more substance to them. I would make a batch every other day, which would be enough for two servings one day and another two servings the next. Each serving had 600-700 calories, meaning she would get up to 1,400 calories per day. I often would get her a McDonald's shake as a special treat at suppertime. It added 700 more calories to her intake for a total of about 2,000 calories per day.

Was it stressful watching her closely to make sure she didn't choke on anything? Absolutely! I was worried every time I put something in her mouth. However, the alternative was watching her waste away, and that was absolutely unacceptable.

Annie was able to use a straw and drink smoothies for the three years we relied on them for her nourishment. She finally needed a feeding tube late in her journey when her brain was definitely failing, but she didn't want one. The Lewy bodies had built up to a level in her brain that made it too difficult to overcome, no matter how hard we tried.

The roller coaster of blood pressure

(Note: The following comes from our experience. It may or may not be appropriate in your case. Talk to your doctor for specific guidance.)

Autonomic dysfunction is a fancy term that means your body is having trouble performing activities it should be able to do automatically. The autonomic nervous system, which we take for granted, is in charge of controlling a number of functions including blood pressure. Autonomic dysfunction is a common occurrence in people with Lewy body diseases such as Parkinson's as various parts of the brain gradually become affected. Functions as basic as maintaining the proper blood pressure so you don't pass out, bladder control, swallowing, and sleeping suddenly become a daily challenge. We take autonomic bodily functions for granted until they don't work, and then it can spell disaster.

I certainly had an advantage in that my medical training prepared me for some of these issues, but even an orthopedic surgeon like me was not prepared for everything we encountered. There were days in which I found myself asking, "My goodness, what is happening today?" This is common in the care of individuals with Parkinson's. Thankfully, experience goes a long way toward taking fast and correct actions, and I'll share a few tips with you in a minute that will give you a head start on your own preparation.

We all have to be alert to every little change, every little indication of a potential problem along our journey. Some of these challenges are fairly common, but some caught me by surprise. For example, one day our care assistant, Sally Ann, called me when I was out running errands to say she couldn't wake up Annie. Having dealt with short episodes like this before with her, I knew what questions to ask.

"Is she breathing okay?"

"Yes."

"Is her color okay?"

"Yes."

"How is her pulse?"

"Strong."

"Did she fall?"

"No, she's sitting at the kitchen table, finishing her oatmeal."

I drove home and Annie remained like that for another forty-five minutes. Since she had a good, strong pulse, I did not think to check her blood pressure. I texted her neurologist and asked him to call me right away. Ten minutes later, the doorbell rang and he was there. He examined Annie and his findings were the same as mine. I continued to shake her every so often and finally she started to wake up. Her neurologist checked her again and could not find anything wrong.

Eight months later, I was watching a webinar at the kitchen table on a Friday. Sally Ann was in the bedroom with Annie, and it was time to administer her medications. It was 2:30 in the afternoon and Annie had been taking a nap. Sally Ann came out and told me she could not wake her up again.

I asked the same series of questions. The only difference was this time Annie was lying down in bed rather than sitting up. Again, I didn't initially take her blood pressure because she had a strong pulse. I called her primary care doctor, who said he'd be right over. Before he arrived, I took her blood pressure (BP) and it was a startlingly high 220/110. (Anything over 150/90 is considered elevated.) For a ninety-pound woman, she was at high risk for a stroke. I even wondered if the blood pressure cuff was on right or operating correctly. I checked Sally Ann's blood pressure and my own, and we were normal. I had seen Annie have trouble waking up before, but not for as long as we were seeing here.

I had never checked her blood pressure before, because she always had a good pulse. Significantly elevated blood pressure that occurs when a person is lying down is called supine hypertension, and it is due to dysfunction of the autonomic nervous system.

Annie never had high blood pressure before that we were aware of. In retrospect, this was likely a case of autonomic hypertension. In other words, the autonomic nervous system in her brain was malfunctioning. Her brain, even with high blood pressure, was not receiving enough blood. That high blood pressure was taking away her brain's ability to function properly.

Her primary care physician arrived and also checked her blood pressure. He found the same 220/110 reading. All of a sudden, she started to come around. The doctor suggested we give her one of my own blood pressure pills to jump-start her autonomic system and bring her blood pressure down to a safe level. I put the pill in some apple sauce and she slowly began to swallow the mixture. Her reading came down to 150/90 within about fifteen minutes, and a half an hour later it was down to a normal 120/70.

The next morning when she was awake in bed, I took her BP and it was 220/110 again.

"What the heck is going on?" I wondered.

I gave her another one of the blood pressure pills, and again she was back to doing okay within a short period of time. I brought her out to the breakfast table and made some oatmeal for her. I was helping her eat when all of a sudden her head slumped forward. I went through the checklist again. She was pale, and her pulse was so weak I could barely feel it. I quickly took her blood pressure and it was only 50/20. That taught me right then not to use blood pressure pills in trying to manage her blood pressure. Body positioning was the key. If her blood pressure was too high, I would have her sit up. If it was too low, I would lie her down immediately and elevate her legs. She would wake up rapidly with this body positioning strategy. (Again, this was what worked for Annie. Consult your doctors for appropriate advice in your case.)

Annie probably passed out on me at least one hundred times over the course of her journey, the vast majority of the times it was due to hypotension (low blood pressure). Fainting wasn't a problem until more than twenty years after her diagnosis, and then really increased about five years after that. I had to learn how to recognize her risk factors and what to do when this happened. I learned day to day what was happening with regard to Annie's blood pressure. I eventually concluded there were two primary circumstances that could lead to a fainting spell. Annie typically would either be sitting somewhere warm or had just eaten. At first, her lethargic condition made me think she was falling asleep.

"Annie, are you okay?" I would ask her.

No response. A check of her pulse found it could be weak. Her body had increased the blood circulation to her gut, shortchanging the blood supply to her brain. Lying her down was the most effective antidote to a hypotensive (low blood pressure) episode, and she often would come around within less than a minute.

One day, she wanted to go out on our back patio and sit in the sun on a warm, humid day. I came in the house for a few minutes, and she was okay when I went back outside to check on her. I told her five more minutes and we would bring her back in the shade. This time when I went back outside, there was no response. She had passed out. I quickly laid her down on the concrete and she responded right away. I realized that from then on, I would have to keep a pad nearby so I wouldn't have to lay her on the concrete. I also paid more attention to limiting the time she spent in locations where it might be too warm for her system.

Keeping her hydrated and cool were keys to keeping her blood pressure in check, especially during warm summer days. Dehydration can have significantly more adverse effects for a Parkinson's patient than for a healthy person. Indeed, it can aggravate or even bring on low blood pressure in a person dealing with autonomic dysfunction challenges. Healthy people can wake up feeling lightheaded and thirsty, but we won't pass out like a Parkinson's patient might. It was an example of how caring for a Parkinson's patient is a constant education. You go from treating a problem to preventing a problem. I saw my job as preventing problems.

Such is the spectrum of autonomic dysfunction. Sometimes it just happens without an obvious cause. The control mechanisms for our blood pressure are so automatic that we don't think about it until there is a problem. Lewy bodies (clumps of abnormal proteins) build up in the nerves involved in controlling the autonomic nervous system just like they can cause problems within the brain. They can affect everything from blood pressure to mood.

With special attention to safety and monitoring her always-changing Parkinson's symptoms, Annie was able to live an active, high quality of life long into her journey. Here she is at the NEW Zoo outside of Green Bay in August 2008 with grandchildren (from left) Zita, Claudia, Carter, Ingrid, Connor, and Heidi.

About half of individuals with advanced Parkinson's disease will experience some of these types of symptoms. As their care partner, you need to be aware this can happen and have a basic understanding of the proper actions to take, because your doctor won't be there. We are taught in medical school to check the ABCs of airway, breathing, and circulation when someone loses consciousness. This is not something that comes up often – if ever – in daily life, until you are faced with this problem all of a sudden.

"Wake up, Rolf," I scolded myself. "It's the ABCs!"

Ensuring your care person is receiving sufficient oxygen to their brain is critical. Permanent damage to the brain can occur after just four minutes without oxygen, and death not long after that.

I would add the letter D to that ABC acronym, and that means "Don't move them" if they fall and hit their head. You have to guard against the possibility there is an associated neck injury, moving them only enough to stabilize their vital signs.

Make sure you have a blood pressure cuff and stethoscope handy. They will be the tools you need to understand these problems and treat them as they arise. Practice using them and learn what your care person's normal blood pressure range is. Learn how to check for a pulse.

This way, when an incident occurs, you will be able to first check to confirm the person has a pulse and then take their blood pressure. If their blood pressure is too high, what we learned worked best for us was to elevate Annie's head and position her body as upright as possible. If the reading is too low or the pulse is very weak pulse, I would lie her down and elevate her feet. Low blood pressure is far more common of an issue. Remember that gravity is your friend when it comes to blood pressure issues. It should take much less than a minute after you adjust your care person's position for them to begin to regain consciousness.

I didn't think to take Annie's blood pressure when these events occurred at first because she had good color and a strong pulse. She only had a couple of high blood pressure events during her journey, while she had more than a hundred low blood pressure events.

I learned that Annie would often have her episodes of low blood pressure in the morning. Her skin would have a greenish tint because the small arteries in her face were not getting enough blood. There wasn't enough oxygen-rich blood coming into her face. More importantly, that oxygen-rich blood was not making it to her brain, causing her to faint. Interestingly, we never detected high blood pressure the last year of her life.

In summary, if your care person's pulse is weak, that tells you their blood pressure is probably low (hypotension). You should lie them down and elevate their feet. Supine hypertension is the opposite of that. This is when you need to position your care person so their body will adapt and automatically lower their blood pressure. We're assuming here that repositioning will take care of the problem. I learned I needed to sit Annie up in these rare instances instead of lying her down. The worst thing I could do with supine hypertension was give Annie a blood pressure pill. This made her blood pressure go down too much and too quickly.

Practice and preparation will help you remain calm. Understand this is basic first aid and not advanced medicine. Talk to your doctor and make the effort to learn about these important facets of care. You won't be able to get to the doctor or call an ambulance fast enough to apply first aid, so you need to take action immediately yourself when these situations arise. You can do this. Be prepared for every step. Have a chair handy if you need to get the individual sitting upright or prop them up in bed if that is where they are. Likewise, have a blanket ready for when you have to lay them on the floor.

Most of these types of challenges turn out okay. The body is amazingly resilient as long as you put it in the correct positions. But when your care person's brain is not functioning correctly, which is the case with autonomic dysfunction, you have to be prepared to deal with it.

We are all different, an experiment of one in everything we do. You have to know yourself and your own capabilities; you have to know your care partner and understand what their needs are; and you have to understand how you can take care of those needs. Most importantly, you have to take action when necessary.

Care partners will often say, "I didn't think of that."

You can put yourself in position to more often say, "I was ready for that."

Tips for making the most of your journey

Maintaining a good quality of life is the most important goal of your care partnership. Annie and I learned many things during our Parkinson's journey, including some I wish I would have realized sooner than later. Acting with tact, love, and understanding to avoid creating more problems is one of them. Our journey was such a joyous experience in many ways. The word "spiritual" means different things to different people, but I feel this was a spiritual journey for us as much as a physical one.

Here are some thoughts to keep in mind as you go through your own journey:

Use the acronym KISS – This stands for "keep it simple, stupid." There is no benefit from overcomplicating things, either for you or your care person. You have enough on your plate without creating unnecessarily complex care strategies.

Always have something to look forward to – We realized early on how helpful it was to have something to pull us both forward. We used weddings, trips, visits to our Florida condo, watching and often attending football and basketball games, and other activities to keep us engaged with life.

Balance your care focus – Your care person will be able to participate in their own care through the early stages of their decline, but at some point you will notice more of that responsibility shifting toward you as their care partner. The challenge as this plays out is to take care of yourself as well as your care person. You will be of little help to your care person if you neglect your own physical and mental health.

This is about them – Try to understand what your care person is going through by imagining yourself in their place. It may help you provide a more effective level of care with the heightened sense of empathy this creates. The more I think about this, the more I realize Annie and I became more united as the amount of care became more demanding. Find a way to make a situation as positive as possible for your care person, and it will be positive for you as well.

Win the war against stress – Stress can make the disease worse, so do your best to not let it control your life. It can become a destructive cycle in which stress makes the symptoms worse, and the symptoms make the stress worse. Share your stress with others in your family and on your care team. Interactions with trusted friends and family are good medicine for stress.

I used running and golf to help me in my battle against stress, even though I largely was not aware of how truly stressed I was. Annie was adamant about these activities remaining a part of my life, regardless of the status of her health.

"You are golfing. You will always be golfing," she told me. "I won't let you give up that membership."

I knew I had to keep myself in good shape for Annie, and I did not want to burden our kids with her care if something were to happen to me. Sally Ann was there enough to help me decompress, too. The kids realized how difficult things were. They wouldn't bring it up with me, but they knew.

Hug, play, and pray – It is so important to keep positive thoughts and activities a constant in your life. You can control so little when it comes to Parkinson's disease that you have to take advantage of things you can control. I often say that one of my biggest regrets is Annie and I hugged a lot, but I wish we would have hugged even more. Hugs can be a healing force in bad moments and turn things around when you're having a bad day. I learned that anxiety was a real issue, not something she could control, and that hugs were the best medicine to soothe those episodes.

Hope is a good medicine – Annie is a great example of how you can have a fulfilling life despite all the challenges that Parkinson's disease presents. Her life was not over at the time of diagnosis by a long shot. We had more than three decades of love and life to share after that moment.

Build trust – Trust is so critical to your care journey. Your care person must be able to entrust you with their care at every level, and that is something you as a care partner must work to strengthen at every opportunity.

Motivation and praise – The best treatment for the apathy that eventually accompanies Parkinson's disease is consistent motivation and praise from the care partner. Find ways to make therapy fun, whether that is walking or swallowing or yelling the alphabet. Stimulate your care person's brain and look for positives in the moment. Many times, especially late in the journey, your care person will not be aware that they don't care. Find little things to praise so that the entire experience is sugar-coated.

Learn to adapt – We didn't stop living, but we did have to adapt to how we lived. Annie had to adapt, therefore I had to adapt with her. We even made adaptations to our home in the spirit of safety, including modifications to our main bathroom in about 2010. Adapting to her changing needs meant always focusing on: 1) preventing falls; 2) keeping her moving; 3) keeping her happy.

Do's for care persons

- Do accept as much love and assistance from your care partner and family as possible.
- Do understand (as much and for as long as possible) that you will not be aware of changes as they gradually occur. As we get older, we don't smell ourselves. Tell your kids, "If I start smelling badly, let me know." Even laugh about it!
- Do guide your care partner. You are in charge of your care as long as you are able. The great thing about caring for Annie is she really guided me to see her needs. Care is a two-way street.
- Do challenge your disease. Understand that your condition is not your fault, not your care partner's fault, and not your doctor's fault. The symptoms can drive you crazy in the moment, but you can take actions that help in the long term.
- Do count your blessings. Make every experience as good as possible or even better. Try to avoid putting limitations on things despite the fact limitations are a reality with Parkinson's disease. Make your reality better.

Do's for care partners

Patience is the foundation of everything you do as a care partner. With that in mind, here are a few tips I learned during our journey:

- Do keep things simple. Just because you can make an activity or strategy complicated, doesn't mean you should. Use language such as "Let's find something we can do to make this fun," rather

Annie with Susan (left) and Sarah at Andy and Elizabeth's wedding in Stowe, Vermont, on October 4, 2014.

than "I want you to do (whatever)." That sounds like an order and generates misunderstanding and defiance.

- Do realize everything won't always go according to plan. For example, I did everything in my power to prevent Annie from falling. I was successful 99 percent of the time, but you can never guarantee perfection.
- Do enjoy the present. Annie and I realized our life would never go back to being as it was, but we were able to build memories along our journey anyway. We took trips abroad, increasingly supported by her travel chair, and enjoyed dozens of trips over many years to our Florida condo.
- Do come up with ways to adapt as your situation changes. For example, we adapted to mobility issues with the use of a travel chair and conducted team showers to prevent falls.
- Do take care of your own physical and emotional health. Coping with stress and depression can be as much a part of being a care partner as it is for your care person. Find family members and friends with whom you can share your feelings, your fears, and your victories. I would run and walk eighteen holes of golf. This helped me control my weight, get in some good exercise, eat sensibly, and come home invigorated.

- Do go with the flow, even if it doesn't make sense sometimes. It can be frustrating, but you will learn to realize the best course of action is proceeding as though the care person is always right.
- Do identify the things that may make a difference in the future. For example, caring for Annie's mouth proved to be a losing battle late in her journey. We couldn't brush her teeth, and the smoothies we used for getting her nutrition were not good for her dental health.
- Do introduce safe activities as a substitute. We liked to bike together until Annie started to experience her falls. I knew I should put guard wheels on her bike, but she would have objected. Plus, they would not necessarily have made her much safer on a bike. Rather than even bring up the idea, we began walking together instead, making sure we always were near a place to sit down.
- Do get your care person to move. Sitting on the couch and watching television does not stimulate the brain, especially with regard to their ability to move. Going to the Y for an hour is great, but what about the rest of the day? Work in the garden, go for a safe walk, or put together a photo album. Do something, anything.
- Do use verbal cues continually. Praise first, then stop, then correct with repeated praiseful instruction.

Don'ts for care partners
Similarly, there are things care partners should avoid in providing support for their care person:
- Don't be judgmental. Your care person is doing the best they can, and that includes with their attitude. Living with Parkinson's disease is a 24/7 challenge, which makes it difficult to remain upbeat at times.
- Don't be hard on yourself or your care person. Cut yourself some slack. No one is perfect either as a care partner or a care person. Instead, look for ways to deliver compliments and positive reinforcement. You both are doing the best you can. Remember, hug often!
- Don't question aggressively. Parkinson's often eventually brings on dementia, and no amount of logic or knowing you are right will change how your care person is thinking. Their brain simply will not be capable of performing as it once did. You may open a can of worms and damage the level of trust you've been working so diligently to build. Lewy body diseases such as Parkinson's

affect different parts of the brain. Some involve memory and mood, both of which do not react well to aggressive questioning.

- Don't seek to control everything. There is only so much you can control, and your care partner will want to retain some level of autonomy as their world largely slips from their control. At the very least, try not to make it obvious you are controlling the situation. Make it your care person's idea and they will be much more likely to cooperate.
- Don't blame yourself or your care partner for your circumstances. Parkinson's disease is nobody's fault, and blaming someone for any of the symptoms they may be experiencing or the stressful situation you may be dealing with is counterproductive.
- Don't get angry. Or at least, don't get so angry that your care person sees it and remembers it. Sometimes things are just so difficult, so frustrating, that you can't help but get a little angry. Believe me, I get that. There will be times when you catch yourself and ask, "Why did I just say that?" That's natural. Just do your best to keep your emotions under control.
- Don't label, as in using the word "disabled." Keep things as positive as possible. Just because a term may be correct doesn't necessarily mean you should use it.
- Don't make a mountain out of a molehill. When things don't work, learn from the experience and look for something else that does work.
- Don't think in terms of "never" or "always." Things are seldom that cut and dried.
- Don't give up.

Resources to consult

- The Boston University CTE Center, which is well-known for its research into the effects of head trauma causing chronic traumatic encephalopathy (CTE), provides a trove of research on its website (https://www.bu.edu/cte/). Its UNITE brain bank is the largest tissue repository in the world focused on traumatic brain injury (TBI) and CTE. I will share the story of my interaction with the Boston University CTE Center as it pertained to learning more about Annie's pathologic evidence later in this book.
- Parkinson's disease received a major publicity jolt when actor Michael J. Fox announced in 1998 that he had been diagnosed in 1991 at the age of twenty-nine. He established The Michael

J. Fox Foundation for Parkinson's Research in 2000. The foundation's website (https://www.michaeljfox.org/) is chock full of information for care partners and care persons alike.

- Davis Phinney is another powerful voice in the Parkinson's world. A former champion cyclist who was the second American to win a stage at the Tour de France, Phinney was diagnosed with Parkinson's at the age of forty. His foundation's website (https://davisphinneyfoundation.org/) also features an extensive collection of information. His book, *Every Victory Counts*, includes separate editions for care partners and care persons. The books focus on proactive self-care and a holistic approach to managing Parkinson's disease.

- Mayo Clinic in Rochester, Minnesota, is a leader in the treatment of Alzheimer's disease and other neurological disorders. Its information base (https://www.mayoclinic.org/diseases-conditions/alzheimers-disease/symptoms-causes/syc-20350447) is the gold standard, and many care partners dealing with the dementia aspect of their care person's journey find this useful.

- Here is a good article pertaining to the benefits of neuroplasticity: *Exercise-enhanced Neuroplasticity Targeting Motor and Cognitive Circuitry in Parkinson's Disease*, a review paper by G.M. Petzinger, et al, 2013. (https://www.ncbi.nlm.nih.gov/pmc/articles/PMC3690528/).

- Several state and national organizations focused on Parkinson's disease offer an incredible amount of information on their websites. Here are three worth checking out:
  - Wisconsin Parkinson Association at https://wiparkinson.org/
  - Parkinsons.org at: http://www.parkinsons.org/
  - American Parkinson Disease Association at: https://www.apdaparkinson.org/

Chapter 7

Back to Back to Back

The end of the 1990s and first decade of the 2000s saw a continuation of our children's personal, educational, and professional journeys. While typically a positive for our kids, dealing with change was a source of stress for Annie, even if it did not directly affect us.

Sarah and her husband were looking for a place to live in Wisconsin as they prepared to return from Utah in 1999 and continue their medical training. Annie and I were in Milwaukee for a weekend event in February and drove through some neighborhoods near the medical complex to see if there were any homes for sale. We happened to drive by a neat little house that had a sign out front: "House for sale by owner." We called the phone number on the sign and the homeowner answered. He mentioned he had just put the sign up and told us the asking price. Annie and I couldn't believe our ears.

"That's a bargain," I said. "The place looks so neat and the location is great. We have to let the kids know about this NOW!"

We went back and toured the house and it was awesome. We called our son-in-law's parents, and they agreed that it sounded good.

"Hopefully, it will be available for a while," they said.

We were convinced the house was not going to be available for a while, because there was already somebody very interested who would be touring the house that afternoon.

To cut to the chase, I bought the house. The realtor with whom the kids were working was not happy. The kids took over our offering and bought the house from us. They loved it during the time they were there. The couple who lived next door even became surrogate grandparents and continue as great friends of our entire family. Sarah and her family moved back to Green Bay in 2002, which made Annie very happy.

Andy and his wife lived in Milwaukee while finishing their studies and working. Their first child was born in May 2003, and several weeks later we helped them with their move to Southern California for their post-graduate training programs. The 2,100-mile drive that Andy and I took with their dog and all of their belongings was a full three-day affair. We had overnight stops in Kansas City with Susan and Monty, and another in Utah. We visited Andy and his family every year for the three years they lived in California.

My brother and his wife lived halfway between Los Angeles and Santa Barbara, so we got the chance to see them as well. We even drove with them up to San Francisco for orthopedic meetings, which gave us some nice time to connect. Andy and I repeated the moving process in reverse three years later when they returned to Wisconsin.

Susan and Monty met in Kansas City, where they both worked at the same engineering firm. They are the oldest of the three couples and gave us our first two grandsons. Susan is the family photographer and photo archivist. Even though they live in Overland Park, Kansas, they love all of the family activities including Ironman competitions and marathon running.

Our family grew to include eight grandchildren and was a joyous experience, especially for Annie and me. However, the stresses of family logistics and the advancing symptoms of Annie's Parkinson's disease created a string of challenges during this period, punctuated by severe back issues that led to a series of surgeries.

Early in 1999, Annie and I flew out to Vail, Colorado, with another couple from our clinic for an orthopedics conference. I hit the slopes to do a little skiing during a break, and when I returned to our room, Annie was unable to get to the door to let me in.

"I can't get out of bed," I heard her say through the door.

I got another key from the front desk and found that Annie's back pain, which increasingly had become more of an issue, had really flared up. We didn't realize that her Parkinson's was playing a role in what would become a decade of significant back issues. Muscle tightness is symptomatic of Parkinson's, and in Annie's case, this was placing an increasing amount of stress on the structures of her spine. She had the classic Parkinson's symptoms of tremors and other challenges with motor skills, but she also had muscle tightness that was out of control.

Here was a 100-pound, beautiful lady with no arthritis in her back, and all of a sudden she has a ruptured disk that applied pressure to a nerve and caused a foot drop to develop. This is a condition in which a person is unable to lift the front of their foot, causing them to drag it when they walk. It seemed she did not experience a lot of pain until it turned significant, and then it was a ten on a scale of one to ten. We tried treating her with anti-inflammatory medications and pain pills, but that was not getting us anywhere.

We were fortunate in that one of the best back surgeons in the state practiced right in Green Bay. Dr. Chris Van Saders was a colleague of mine at Prevea Clinic (pronounced Pre-VAY-uh), and we would count on his expertise for a series of surgeries during the course of the next ten-plus years.

Chris did an MRI on Annie that showed she had a ruptured disc pressing on a nerve. Annie underwent her first surgery (a partial discectomy) for a ruptured disk in her lower back (the lumbar region) on July 30, 1999. The procedure relieved her pain and alleviated pressure on the nerve root that was causing the drop foot issue.

Annie felt okay with regard to her back for the rest of 1999, but then she experienced terrible pain again early in 2000. She was just miserable. We tried injections to relieve her pain, but eventually Chris informed us the disk between her L4 and L5 vertebrae had collapsed and the injections would not be a viable long-term solution. He would have to fuse those vertebrae as well, meaning she was now fused from the L4 to the L5 vertebrae in her lower back.

This time, the stabilization procedure really seemed to help and she did well with regard to back pain for the next several years. Chris did not have to fuse the lowest vertebra in Annie's lumbar region (L5) to the sacrum (S1) located just below it. (The sacrum is the large, flat, triangular-shaped bone located between the hip bones.) That was the good news. The bad news is when you fuse vertebrae like Chris had to do for Annie, the stress that those disks previously would have absorbed transfers to the next level up. It was likely only a matter of time until physics took its toll.

"The problem with spines is you are never able to truly fix everything," Chris explains. "The analogy I use is it's like putting out a fire in the forest, and then hoping it doesn't reignite there or in a different spot in the forest. We can fuse one level and take care of that problem, but then the adjacent levels can become more problematic. People with Parkinson's disease are at higher risk because the muscle imbalances they have can't protect the levels of the spine that haven't been fused as well as someone who doesn't have a neuromuscular issue."

Chris did, indeed, have to complete Annie's back fusion from L2 through the sacrum – basically from part way down her back into her sacrum on

Looking good during our August 2009 trip to the US Open Tennis Championships in New York. This was eight months after Annie's fifth back surgery.

February 7, 2005. He used metal rods to provide temporary support and enable the bone fusions to take hold, along with bone grafts to strengthen the biological portions of the remaining spine.

We had gotten six months of relief out of the first operation, five years out of the second, and would get almost two years out of this third operation. We were relieving Annie's pain for the time being, but were far from out of the woods. The combination of her Parkinson's disease, physics, and human anatomy meant this would turn out to be a recurring issue. We could only hope to avoid more serious consequences as long as possible.

Pain issues began to increase for Annie again in the fall and early winter of 2006, and by December, her condition forced Chris to fuse her L1 and L2 vertebrae. We were good for another two years until the very end of 2008. Annie had been experiencing more pain again, when all of a sudden in the middle of the night, her pain became intolerable and she couldn't move. Her legs were very weak and now we had a potential disaster on our hands. I called Chris and he performed an emergency decompression procedure on New Year's Day morning 2009.

"This is only temporary," Chris informed me. "I'm going to have to do extensive spinal fusion to decompress from here up."

Annie had recovered fairly well after two weeks, but Chris had to make sure there was enough room for her spinal cord within the fused spinal column. Any compromise to the spinal cord could result in paralysis. That prospect was terrifying. So on January 15, 2009, he decompressed her spine again, this time fusing her solidly from T3 in the upper back all the way down through her lower back. Virtually her entire spine was now fused.

This procedure proved relatively successful for the next two years or so as her Parkinson's decline continued to progress. Then, starting in the winter of 2011-12, she began exhibiting some neurological symptoms, including pain down into her legs in addition to her back. She seemed to have some weakness in her feet as well, but not dramatically so.

We were struggling with her medications at this time, and her neurologist suggested she may benefit from deep brain stimulation in treating her Parkinson's. We secured an appointment for an evaluation at Froedtert Hospital in Milwaukee, which is about two hours from our house. The neurologist at Froedtert told us Annie was not a candidate for deep brain stimulation – and we didn't want to insert wires into her brain at this point anyway – because the spasms in her legs were not a result of her Parkinson's. He believed her spinal cord was being compromised.

We returned to Green Bay, and Chris examined updated images of Annie that showed the support rods in her back had broken. The fusion was no longer solid at one level of her back and there was no extra room for her spinal cord to pass through. Every time her spine shifted, it was irritating her spinal cord and causing issues such as pain and leg spasms.

Our Green Bay neurologist examined Annie at home, and his message to me mirrored that of Chris's a week earlier: "Watch her like a hawk." We couldn't afford any type of violent movement such as a fall, because that could spell doom.

We were okay until early in the morning of Wednesday, March 7, 2012, when Annie told me she had to go to the bathroom. I went over to her side of the bed and asked her to move her legs closer to me so I could help her up.

"I can't," she said.

"Can you feel me touching you?" I asked.

"No."

Annie was paralyzed.

I didn't care if it was five in the morning. I called Chris right away and told him what was happening. He told me to call an ambulance and have her transported across town to his home base of St. Mary's Hospital Medical Center. He would need to get some special equipment in before he could operate the following day, March 8, 2012.

I was panicked. I was worried this may be permanent paralysis for Annie and an end to her reasonably good quality of life.

Chris decompressed her spine during the long surgery on Thursday, and then re-fused her with new metal rods. Annie showed no improvement on Friday. There was no change on Saturday. I was privately crying, praying and praying. I knew spinal cord shock – which is what Annie had – takes a little while to recover. It's like the spinal cord goes to sleep as the body tries to protect it. The question is whether the "sleep" is temporary or permanent.

That Sunday morning, our version of a miracle happened.

"Hi, honey," I said upon entering her room. I pulled back the covers to reveal her legs and feet. "Wiggle your feet up and down."

To my great joy, she did!

I cried and we hugged as I looked upward.

"God, thank you!"

From that point until her passing in 2021, we never had a problem with Annie's back again. We were so blessed. Her quality of life improved dramatically and she could now stand on her own. We were able to travel extensively, cheering on Andy as he competed in the Ironman Wisconsin competition in Madison in 2011, and then in Hawaii the next year for the Ironman World Championships. A full Ironman consists of a 2.4-mile swim, a 112-mile bicycle ride, and a full running marathon of 26.2 miles for a total of 140.6 miles.

Our family banded together to raise awareness for Parkinson's disease at Ironman Wisconsin. We had t-shirts made for everyone to wear that featured a family picture and the words "Team Annie L" across the bottom. We raised more than $23,000 as a group and donated the funds to the Michael J. Fox Foundation.

The Ironman Wisconsin race was hot and extremely challenging for all the participants, and even an experienced competitor like Andy really struggled to complete the event.

"I've never seen you suffer like that," I told Andy afterward. "What kept you going?"

"Mom kept me going," he responded.

We turned the Hawaii trip into a wonderful family vacation. We flew first class to give Annie some extra room and comfort on the plane. Andy took his three kids, and Susan came along to help. My brother Kim's oldest son, Kris, traveled with us and was very helpful.

We also went to New York for the US Open Tennis Championships, and flew one more time to Europe. Our last significant trip came in 2015 when Susan's husband, Monty, competed in an Ironman in Coeur d'Alene, Idaho. We flew into Portland, Oregon, to visit some friends in the area, including some old Fort Dix friends in Spokane, Washington.

Every one of Annie's seven back operations was a major procedure. There were no minor clean-ups here. She was devastated each time it

Team Annie L at Ironman Wisconsin in 2011. Our family raised more than $23,000 to donate to the Michael J. Fox Foundation in honor of Annie.

became apparent she needed another operation even though she knew they needed to be done. She was especially down prior to one of her surgeries.

I said, "Annie, I'm not on call this weekend. Let's go to Chicago."

We stayed in a nice hotel for two nights, ate at the restaurant there, and brought along a travel chair so we could shop a little bit. Annie had to go to the restroom as we were leaving the restaurant one evening, and she needed my help at this point in her journey. We headed toward the ladies room, which alarmed a woman near the door.

"You can't go in there!" she scolded me.

"In that case, would you help my wife?" I asked her.

"You can go in there," she replied sheepishly.

Annie had the operation that Tuesday and it was like she was a new person. Her pain level was gone. She tolerated pain very well, but when she was hurting, you knew it.

Annie had seven back operations in the 2000s with six months of recovery after each one, adding up to forty-two months that she was struggling just with this issue alone. Was that stressful? You bet it was. In looking over her 300-plus pages of medical records, it is obvious that she was really struggling during the decade of spinal operations. I don't blame her for being emotionally overwhelmed.

There is no question Chris Van Saders saved the quality of her life with the procedures he performed, and for that we are forever indebted to him. I don't know what we would have done if we didn't have Chris on our team.

Chapter 8

The Frontier of Medicine

Early in 2016, I read an interesting article in the *Wall Street Journal's* book section that really caught my attention. It was a two-page introductory piece discussing a book entitled *The Brain's Way of Healing: Remarkable Discoveries and Recoveries from the Frontiers of Neuroplasticity*, written by a psychiatrist and researcher from Toronto named Norman Doidge, MD. The book includes strategies and techniques you can use to improve brain function in people who have experienced strokes, multiple sclerosis (MS), Parkinson's disease, and potentially those with traumatic brain injuries.

I thought, "I've got to get that book!" I called our local Barnes & Noble and they had it, so I went there right away and bought a copy.

The book includes the story of Ron Husmann, a Broadway performer who had gradually lost his singing voice and ability to control his bladder before ultimately receiving a diagnosis of multiple sclerosis. One of Husmann's high school friends lived in Madison, Wisconsin, where a team was experimenting with something called a PoNS™ ("pahns" for short) device in a lab at the University of Wisconsin. PoNS, which stands for Portable Neuromodulation Stimulator, is a device that sends electrical stimulation signals to the patient's tongue, and the nerves there pass along that stimulation to the brain. In effect, the PoNS device uses electrical impulses to reset the brain.

Husmann traveled to Madison for two weeks of treatments with the PoNS device, coupled with intensive speech therapy sessions. He was singing and dancing again by the end of his visit. Dr. Doidge attributed this improvement to neuroplastic healing promoted, in part, by the PoNS device.

I had to find out more about this exciting treatment option. I really liked the fact this technique was very low-risk compared to the deep brain stimulation techniques already in use for neurological disorders. However, despite my connections with the university, it still took us nine months to arrange a tour of the lab. The team there was amazing, and I left optimistic that this technique could be helpful for Annie. They had been helping MS and Parkinson's patients, and had wondered if PoNS treatments could be beneficial for traumatic brain injury patients as well.

The device had been approved for use in Canada, but not in the US, so our insurance would not pay for it. (It has since received limited FDA approval in the US.) Regardless, I had seen the evidence of how it had dramatically helped some people and I wanted to try it.

"Whatever you want," Annie said, her Parkinson's apathy strongly intact.

We finally received approval for a May 2019 visit to the Surrey Neuroplasticity Clinic outside of Vancouver, British Columbia. This was more than three years after my initial introduction to PoNS treatments through the *WSJ* article and Dr. Doidge's book, and less than two years prior to Annie's passing. The clinic would not make any promises, of course, about whether it could help someone like Annie with advanced Parkinson's. They wanted us to plan on spending almost three weeks there. We knew this wasn't going to be a cheap trip, but we were pulling for a straw that would work.

"Annie, we're going to do another honeymoon," I told her. "Yes, we're going up there for healthcare reasons, but we're going to relax and enjoy ourselves while we're there."

I bought first-class tickets for us on Delta to Vancouver, and the airline staff took such good care of us. Everybody helped out at every

Here we are with Jill Clark, one of the wonderful staff members who worked with us at the Surrey Neuroplasticity Clinic near Vancouver, Canada.

stage of the trip, and we were able to enjoy a glass of wine with a decent meal on the plane. The clinic staff also was fantastic in how they dealt with Annie, helping this fragile woman through what undoubtedly was a tiring series of therapy sessions. I shot some video of one of the sessions, and the scene is both heartwarming and heartbreaking as Annie was determined as always to give it her best effort.

We stayed in a nice little chain hotel near the clinic and did not venture out to see much of the Vancouver area. You never know how high the beds will be in a hotel room, and getting Annie onto a taller bed by this point was a challenge. She definitely couldn't get up onto this bed by herself. I found a hardware store nearby where I bought a little stool. I put Annie in her travel chair next to the stool, helped her

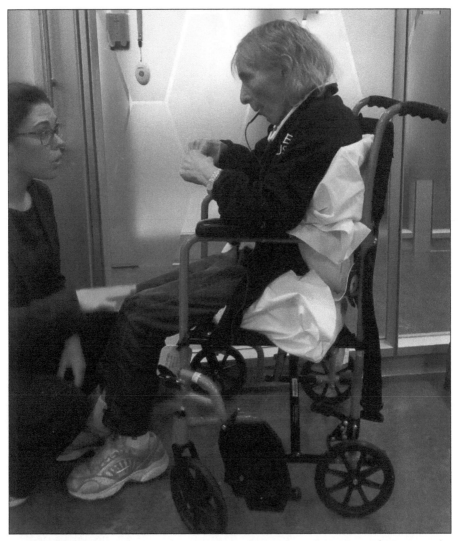

Annie holds the PoNS device in her mouth as she works with Marie-Josée Ryan at the Surrey Neuroplasticity Clinic.

to her feet, turned her ninety degrees and up onto the stool, and then spun her onto the bed. It was another example of how we had to adapt to situations as they arose.

We ate dinner almost every night at a small bar/restaurant next to the hotel. The restaurant staff was wonderful to us. One evening, the Milwaukee Bucks were playing the Toronto Raptors in the Eastern Conference semifinals of the NBA playoffs, and the restaurant was showing the game on its many TVs scattered around the facility. The

Canadian fans were cheering for the Raptors, of course, while we were the only people in the place cheering for our home-state Bucks. It was a fun night and gave us something to focus on besides what was happening at the clinic.

We patronized the restaurant so often that it didn't take long before we became familiar faces to the staff and their regular customers. One night, our waitress had a pleasant surprise for us.

"You don't owe anything tonight," she informed us. "We have a regular customer here, and he has noticed the two of you. He is so impressed that you are out doing things that he wanted to pay for your dinners tonight."

I told her I would really like to thank that person, and she got his permission for us to stop over at his table.

"You two are special," the man said. "You deserve it."

I was able to buy him a drink a couple nights later when we saw him again.

Twice toward the end of our visit, the restaurant itself took care of our tabs. "You've paid your way enough," they told us.

We were on the receiving end of similar experiences several times over the last several years of our journey. One of those instances occurred at an Applebee's in Dubuque, Iowa, the last time we drove to Kansas City to visit Susan and Monty. It was a busy Friday night and the place was packed. Luckily, we were able to get a table without much delay and enjoyed a nice meal.

"We'd like the check now, please," I told our waitress when we were ready to leave.

The waitress left and never returned, so I asked another waitress to see what was going on.

"We have a policy," she explained, "that if any of our staff sees someone special and it's a booming night, we can pick one table and say, 'You're free tonight.' And you are free tonight."

The generosity we experienced at the restaurant in Surrey was one of several aspects of our trip to Canada and the Surrey Neuroplasticity Clinic that made this an overall positive experience. But in the end, the treatments did not seem to have any benefit for Annie. She was likely too far along in her journey at that point, her brain too badly damaged.

Chapter 9

Coming to the End of Our Journey

The last three years of Annie's journey was crunch time. We could tell the end was coming and we had to make the activities of daily living (ADLs) as safe as possible. We learned to adapt to her symptoms. Maintaining your lifestyle to the highest extent possible is hugely important, because that is the only way to treat the disease.

We found many ways to turn a bad situation – or at least a less than ideal situation – into a good one. For example, it was not safe for her to get into the shower with me toward the end of her life, so we had our caregiver, Sally Ann, help us in that regard. I put on my swimsuit, and between the two of us, we got Annie scrubbed from her head to her toes, and she was okay with that.

Prior to this, I almost had a naivety with regard to her condition, even with how she looked. I loved her so much and was so close to her that I didn't notice the extent to which she was going downhill. Her nutrition was declining along with her swallowing challenges, and in retrospect we should have been much more aggressive about that. Regardless, I have to admit it probably would have been too little, too late to have resulted in any improvement.

Annie started to sleep more and more, and we got hospice involved in June of 2020. I thought this might be premature, but the hospice folks and our kids urged us to take this step. The staff did a good job of guiding us, taking control of her medications, and being available for any special needs that came up.

The difficult part was having Annie sign the paperwork giving me healthcare power of attorney. Downplaying this administrative step for the care person's sake is a good way to minimize the emotional aspect. I have signed over my healthcare power of attorney to the kids, and I had no problem doing that. I encourage you to have this paperwork on file regardless of your age or health status. This ensures your loved ones can make decisions on your behalf in the event you lose the capacity to do so.

The same goes for final arrangements. I am a believer in taking care of as many details ahead of time as possible so your final wishes take place without survivors arguing or stressing over them. My family's funeral home background likely makes it easy for me to think about such things.

Annie and I had this discussion a good twenty years before she passed. We attended the funeral of a man who died of cancer, and the subject came up afterward when the two of us went out to dinner. It was a chilly winter night and we were relaxing with a cocktail.

"Annie, we've never really talked about this," I began, "but going to this funeral today makes me think that we should talk about arrangements sometime for when we pass away."

Annie had full-blown Parkinson's by this point, so it was natural for her to be thinking of her own demise.

"What do you mean?" she asked.

"Well, would you want to be embalmed and buried, or would you want to be cremated?" I asked. "I don't think the kids should make the decisions. They should know what we want."

"I don't want to talk about it," she said sternly.

"I respect that, Annie. Some of us don't want to think about those things," I said, and then changed the subject.

Five minutes later, Annie had obviously processed my suggestion.

"In regard to your question," she said, "what would you want done?"

"I would want to be embalmed and buried at Woodlawn Cemetery on the open hill, with no tree over us so the birds won't crap on my grave," I said. "You can see the sunrise and sunset from there. The kids and grandkids can look up on the hill and see the stone and say, 'Hi, Dad. Hi, Grandpa.' "

"I'll do what you do," she stated, and that was the end of that conversation.

We never discussed that topic again.

The final stretch

Near the end, Annie's mouth failed. Her dental hygiene was terrible. How do you brush the teeth of someone who cannot swallow or spit safely? She couldn't open her mouth very much and objected to any help. I kept making her smoothies to get her some calories, yet bacteria love the environment of a warm, moist mouth. Yes, it was a pain making smoothies every day, but it was keeping her alive and a far better alternative than a feeding tube.

Annie had a few cake crumbs on her lips when we took this family picture on August 7, 2019, about a year and a half before she passed.

Recall that I have two regrets when it comes to Annie: we hugged a lot, but we still didn't hug enough; and I didn't identify certain aspects of her decline until it was too late to make a difference. Now, would I actually have been able to make a difference? I don't know, but I would have liked to have tried.

Looking back, I actually have one more regret. I didn't take good enough care of her mouth. I don't know if she would have accepted my help and coaching, but she may have gotten used to it and it may have extended her life. Oral health for Parkinson's patients is a critical component of overall health, just as it is for those of us lucky enough to enjoy good health. Parkinson's had taken away Annie's ability to chew and swallow well, but it also created a level of calmness.

Other aspects of Annie's health gradually deteriorated as well. She woke up one morning a little more than a year before she passed and wanted to go to the bathroom. I said, "Give me your hands and I'll help you up." Her right hand just hung straight down. She had nerve damage referred to as Saturday night palsy. She must have slept in a position that applied pressure to the radial nerve just above the elbow. That continued to be a problem for us the last fourteen months of her life. I tried to splint it straight, but she couldn't tolerate the discomfort and I eventually had to remove it.

The approaching end to a journey as lengthy as Annie's brings with it a wide range of emotions for the primary care partners as well as family and friends. In our case, we hunkered down at home when the COVID pandemic hit in March of 2020. It was just Annie and me in our house. The isolation was overwhelming. Sure, the kids would drop in with masks, Sally Ann would come over twice a week to give me a little respite time, and we had Zoom calls with the family, but we didn't go out and do things anymore.

It seemed that Annie was oblivious to what was going on. Rather than point it out to her, we substituted love for the reality of the times. We snuggled up together, and in a way, the lockdown actually drew us closer together. That part was nice, but there is no doubt the isolation hastened Annie's downward trend.

Annie entered hospice care about this time and was sleeping most of the time. Her dementia left her confused as to what the hospice nurses and aides were even doing there.

"They're just here to help us, Annie," I explained.

We had a quiet family gathering at Christmas that year, and I asked two couples with whom we were close friends to come over for a visit before they headed down to Florida for the winter.

"Come over and see Annie before you go," I said, "because I don't think she'll make it to spring."

Susan made a second trip up from Kansas City about a month after Christmas as well. Annie couldn't be involved in any of the conversations by that point, but she was happy to see everyone. She put a smile on her face as much as she could despite the fact terminal Parkinson's disease makes it damn hard to smile. It's not just because of the underlying depression, apathy, and dementia, it's that your facial muscles just don't work anymore. I can tell the approximate dates pictures were taken just by looking at Annie's face.

By early February of 2021, I realized we may only have a few days left. Annie was sleeping a lot and had her eyes open only once in a while. She watched part of the Super Bowl with me on a Sunday night, and Sarah and her boyfriend came over to visit. Annie was half asleep on the couch when they arrived.

"It's so nice to meet you, Ann," he said.

"Thank you," Annie replied softly, never taking her eyes off him.

The interaction was amazing and sort of peaceful to watch. That was basically the last responsive act she had. I asked her the next morning if she wanted water, and she said no. She never drank anything again. She was at peace.

Annie passed while lying in our bed right next to me at 4 p.m. on Friday, February 12, 2021. That's the way it had to be. After battling Parkinson's for close to forty-five years, the disease finally took away her ability to live on. God so blessed us that she was able to sleep away peacefully, at home, without pain, and without suffering. As tough as it was to lose her physical, loving presence, it was comforting to know she was at peace.

Love, gratitude, and spirituality were our comforts through that last year or so. Her resiliency and toughness were incredible for almost half a century. In looking back, I can find more memories of joy that I hadn't thought about in some time. Some of them were even funny. Annie will always be spectacularly vibrant in my mind's eye. She had a way of making me excited. We just got each other, and her legacy lives on within me. Some people roll their eyes when I say this, but I believe her spiritual presence has not left me even though she has left this physical world.

Wanting to know more

I started thinking about brain donation long before Annie reached the end of her journey. In fact, it was probably ten or fifteen years prior to the end of her life that I looked into it in more detail, in part because of our own family histories.

My mother and brother had Alzheimer's disease, and Annie's brother and mother had Parkinson's disease, although Zita's neurologist felt she just had simple tremors. Annie had been diagnosed only two years prior to my mother's passing at the age of seventy-six in 1991. I didn't dare bring up the subject with Annie. I knew she would be devastated and didn't want her life to be anything other than joy and friends.

My interest in brain health in general was increasing due to the news coming out of the National Football League. Or rather, the news coming from researchers looking at former NFL players, because the league at that time downplayed any information it viewed as detrimental. Before long, however, the avalanche of research left the NFL no choice but to begrudgingly admit there may – and it emphasizes "MAY" – be risks associated with repeated head trauma to the brain.

The first former player to hit the news was Mike Webster, a Hall of Fame center for the Pittsburgh Steelers. A native of Tomahawk, Wisconsin, Webster played collegiately at the University of Wisconsin before being drafted in the fifth round by the Steelers. He played in 245 pro football games, so one can only imagine how many blows to the head he endured while anchoring the middle of the line.

Webster was still a young man when his brain began failing, leading to erratic behavior. By the time he died in 2002 of a heart attack at the age of fifty, he was unmanageable. His wife had divorced him and he was destitute. A neuropathologist who served as an assistant in the Pittsburgh medical examiner's office was the first to discover that Webster's brain was littered with protein clumps that affected its ability to function properly. He reported that Webster's brain showed signs of what he called chronic traumatic encephalopathy (CTE), a progressive brain disease he maintained was caused by repeated traumatic brain injuries such as the concussions and repeated head bangs without true concussions that NFL players endure for many years.

Other players' cases followed, many after deaths by suicide. Still, the NFL did its best to put the clamps on any negative press that might affect its bottom line. A rather unseemly battle for players' brains ensued, with a team at Boston University eventually emerging as the acknowledged experts. A neuropathologist originally from Appleton,

Wisconsin, (and the University of Wisconsin) named Ann McKee, MD, is the lead researcher for an organization called the Boston University CTE Center (Boston Brain Bank, for short). It combines the resources of Boston University, the Veterans Administration, and the Concussion Legacy Foundation.

I was following the research coming out surrounding this new CTE diagnosis with some interest as I often provided the medical coverage at local high school and college football games in my role as an ortho-pedic surgeon. The seriousness of concussions was not yet fully under-stood by the general public, and even some in the medical community. It was not unusual for some coaches to keep players on the field after getting their bell rung, telling them to "be tough" or "shake it off."

One particular episode stands out for me. I was on the sidelines for a high school game in the early 2000s when a player was knocked un-conscious. As I attended to the young man on the field, I requested an ambulance to transport him to the hospital. His coach – an old-school type of guy – was not pleased that one of his star players would be un-available for the rest of the game.

"Come on, doc. Don't overreact," he told me sternly.

Fortunately, the lead official recognized the gravity of the situation and ordered the coach to back off.

"Doc is in charge of the situation," he told the coach.

It was a disturbing example of how some football coaches viewed the issue of concussion and brain injury. Fortunately, things have changed dramatically since then.

In addition to the articles I was reading about CTE research going on at the national level, I was also aware of research taking place at the University of Wisconsin regarding Alzheimer's disease. There is a very active Alzheimer's research initiative in Madison that had started in 2000. They are following a number of volunteer patients and their fam-ilies, and there was even a local film produced that told their stories. These researchers understood that Alzheimer's disease is not simply a function of aging. They were looking at lifestyle issues, imaging studies, levels of exercise, and other variables.

The individuals had all volunteered to donate their brains, which was key in helping the researchers see the complete physiological pic-ture beyond what was possible during the subjects' lifetime using tradi-tional brain scan imaging. I was following their progress intently.

As the end of Annie's life came nearer, the physician in me decided I wanted to know more about what was going on inside her brain. I wondered, should I donate her brain for a scientific investigation into the effects of her Parkinson's disease? Will the kids approve? The last thing I wanted was to have Annie get wind of this, although her cognitive impairment was such by that point that she likely would not have been able to process that.

I had to think this over. This was not something I discussed with anyone else as I wanted to avoid any judgement or drama. The more I thought about it, I decided yes, I've got to do it.

Most importantly, I wanted to work with a top-notch organization, so I contacted the Boston University CTE Center to discuss donating her brain. It was June of 2020 and the COVID pandemic was in full swing. I called the Brain Bank's 800 number and spoke with a representative about Annie's condition.

"My wife has advanced Parkinson's disease, she's seventy-nine years old, and she's had it for about forty-four years," I said. "I'd really like to know what her brain shows.

Annie's eightieth birthday party took place during the COVID pandemic on September 7, 2020. She would pass away five months later.

She's so amazing and we made such a difference."

"Has she ever had any brain trauma?" he asked.

"Yes, she's had three major falls, each with about ten minutes of unconsciousness," I replied.

"Just a second," the man said, and then put me on hold.

A few minutes later, he came back on the line.

"She's in," he said.

I'm certain the brain trauma was the icing on the cake for getting her accepted. They were looking for CTE first and foremost, and they had experience with Alzheimer's disease and other neurological conditions such as Parkinson's. I quietly had conversations about the donation process with our funeral home of choice, Proko-Wall Funeral Home, and the pathologist at St. Vincent Hospital to ensure everything would go smoothly.

"No problem," the St. Vincent pathologist told me. "We know how to prepare it; we just need to know where to send it."

Now it was time to discuss my plans with the kids. I talked to Sarah and Andy first because they worked in healthcare professions. I asked them not to tell anyone else about my plans. I didn't tell Susan right away because I wasn't as convinced she would approve and didn't want to create any turmoil. It turned out I needn't have worried. We were preparing for Annie's celebration of life the summer following her death when I brought up the subject.

"That is so nice," Susan said. "I'm so glad you did that."

All three of our children understood my desire to learn as much as possible about what caused their mother's Parkinson's disease.

When the time came for Annie's journey to come to an end, all the pieces of this logistical puzzle worked as planned. Annie died at four o'clock in the afternoon on Friday, February 12, 2021. Hospice came over and contacted Proko-Wall. The funeral directors arrived and confirmed they knew they were dealing with a donation situation.

"We will embalm tonight, and at six o'clock tomorrow morning, we'll bring her to the hospital lab," they explained. "They will harvest the brain, and then send her brain overnight to Boston. Then we will take her back and continue funeral preparations."

"Why are they going to take Grandma to the hospital?" asked our eleven-year-old grandson, Wally.

"They have to do some tests," I explained, "because she was very sick."

Everybody knew their roles in this important process. It was very user-friendly. I also called the Brain Bank to let them know Annie had passed away, and they reassured me that they were prepared to receive her donation.

The next day, which was a Saturday, we went to the funeral home to make arrangements. Annie's brain was already on ice and placed on a plane to Boston. I received a text about noon on Sunday.

"Dr. Lulloff, your donation has arrived. It is in excellent condition. You have our deepest sympathies. We are so grateful for your donation. We will be in touch with you tomorrow about the details and what you can expect over the next few months."

I received a text Monday morning from Lisa McHale, director of family relations at the CTE Center. Lisa's late husband, Tom, was a lineman for the Tampa Bay Buccaneers and the second NFL player confirmed to have had CTE by the Boston Brain Bank. Lisa called me and we talked for an hour about Annie's history. We hit it off great.

"I will be your contact person," she explained. "You can count on the fact we'll be confidential. We will contact you for all the medical information available for Ann about the middle of July. It takes about nine months to stabilize her brain with chemicals before we can prepare a report. We have two teams working on each case, a pathology team and a clinical team, and they do not communicate with each other so as not to interfere with their professional interpretations of the data and physical findings.

"The clinical team puts together the medical history and diagnostic information. The pathology team doesn't know the clinical history. They are there to determine what the brain pathology shows. The two diagnoses may not be the same, but they will be associated."

It all sounded fascinating to me. I was eager to see their reports.

In the meantime, the Boston team sent questionnaires to Sarah and me to complete. They also wanted to do an hour-long phone interview with us. Sarah and I sat together, and one of the first questions they posed concerned any depression that Annie might have had.

I had tried to minimize some of her symptoms during the course of her journey, including her depression, but I did acknowledge them. Perhaps I didn't truly sense the weight of her depression because I lived with her and was intimately involved with her care.

"How severe was her depression?" the interviewer asked us.

"She was kind of depressed," I answered. "It really wasn't that bad."

"Dad!" Sarah interjected. "It was terrible! She was majorly depressed. You were oblivious to it."

I had become so used to Annie's depression that its severity was lost on me. Panic attacks, anxiety, and depression all result from Lewy body disorders in the brain. It is a progressive affliction that is not consistent in its appearance. The person may have a severe issue for a period of time, and then it may quiet down. Nobody knows why Lewy bodies develop, which is the challenge behind preventing these diseases.

Looking back, Annie's depression and panic attacks had been part of her life for more than fifty years. Our friend, Sue Hollenbeck, observed this first hand.

"I'm terrified in malls," Annie told Sue at one point. "I have to walk next to the wall, I'm so insecure."

Finally, the neuropathology report came back and confirmed Annie suffered from Lewy body disease of the brain. Some people with Lewy body disease don't have Parkinson's symptoms. They have sleep problems, hallucinations, etc. Remember, Annie was confused enough to ask, "Is mother up yet?" when her mother had been dead for several years.

Lisa McHale, my contact at the Boston Brain Bank, called in December (about nine months after Annie's donation) to set up a time for a Zoom call with their pathologist and our family. Susan joined from Kansas City, Andy was unavailable, and I went over to Sarah's to participate together. Boston Brain Bank's Russ Huber, MD, PhD, explained that Annie's clinical diagnosis was Parkinson's disease, while her pathological diagnosis was Lewy body disease of the brain. The wonderful thing about the Boston team is they are looking at all aspects of the puzzle. Russ briefed us on what we would see in the report and answered our questions, and Lisa made sure we received the formal report via email, as well as further follow-up.

The report referenced tau proteins, Lewy bodies, and specified the parts of the brain involved. It is a process of elimination to determine Parkinson's disease based on which proteins are involved and in what form. Since you don't see clumps of Lewy bodies in the brains of Alzheimer's or CTE patients, that leaves Parkinson's as the likely culprit. The researchers saw what we expected to see in that the arteries in Annie's brain were in poor condition, even though her heart had never been a known problem. A surprising finding was that despite the falls that caused her head injuries, she showed no signs of head trauma.

Lewy bodies present in the olfactory bulbs of the brain resulted in her loss of sense of smell, and more Lewy bodies in the substantia nigra portion of her brain contributed to her motor skills deterioration. In addition, tau proteins and tangles in the neuro fibers were consistent with early Alzheimer's and age-related mental decline, also known as Primary Age-Related Tauopathy (PART).

The abnormal cells set the pattern for the next cell down the line, which copies the abnormal protein and keeps it moving like a contagious disease. There is nothing that can be done to stop or reverse these types of neurodegenerative processes, at least at this point.

The neuropathology report was a huge piece of the pie when it came to putting together Annie's story because it confirmed many things. Now we knew why she lost her sense of smell, why she had dementia, why she had hallucinations and delusions. Parkinson's disease gradually took Annie's brain function away. We kept her going with love and prayer. Bad things happen to good people. None of us likes to think about that, but they do.

As care partners, we can all become hypersensitive to our own challenges. I can tell you there were days early on when I wondered if I had Parkinson's disease, too. It's almost like there was a transference from Annie, like it was contagious somehow. Of course it's not contagious, but we are all dealing with a condition called the normal process of aging and there are different manifestations of it. Sometimes it is a disease that is the cause of a person's decline.

For me, my balance isn't that good anymore. I have to focus on that while I'm running or even walking quickly. You have to start doing exercises that benefit your strength, stamina, and balance long before it becomes obvious that you have a problem.

Because I made the decision to donate Annie's brain, I'm able to tell people things that we learned from that study. I didn't want to regret not knowing and later say, "I wish we would have donated her brain."

We gradually became comfortable talking about the donation with friends. Most people are pretty neutral on the topic, but I understand donations of any kind are not for everybody. I respect people who say, "I don't want that done to me." Everyone has their own ideas about the afterlife and how donations may or may not play a role in that.

My personal satisfaction in having made that decision has been awesome. If I had not done that, I would have been angry with myself. Were the results a big surprise? No, but they did give me valuable information and a sense of closure. Furthermore, that information strengthens Annie's legacy in helping so many people understand how much we can do in our lives to impact the world.

I have since made the decision to donate my brain as well. I have my senior moments and I wonder if there is a possibility I am in the early stages of Alzheimer's disease. My brother had Alzheimer's, so I might be a good study subject. I also have other co-morbidity factors such as coronary artery disease, and they will want to look at my heart and liver, too. My dad died of liver failure and he was a late-life diabetic.

My only regret is that I won't be able to see the reports. Hopefully, I'll still know somehow.

***

I firmly believe all of our efforts helped us provide Annie with a high quality of life much longer than she could have enjoyed otherwise. We kept her going for forty-five years after she had her first symptom (loss of sense of smell in 1976), and thirty-one years after she was officially

This likely is one of the last extended family photos we took while Annie was alive. It was during a late fifty-fifth anniversary party for us at Andy and Elizabeth's house on August 7, 2019. Standing are Carter, Heidi, Sarah, Greta, Ingrid, and Monty. Sitting are Elizabeth, Wally, Andy, Annie and me, Susan, Connor, Zita, and Claudia.

diagnosed with Parkinson's disease. We kept her active, engaged, up and about as much as possible, and at home.

We went to Europe and the Caribbean many times. We bought a condominium on Sanibel Island in Florida, visiting there three to five times per year for almost nineteen years. We walked on the beach, hosted friends and family, and enjoyed the change of scenery. Our visits there were like a honeymoon every time. It was a rejuvenation for us.

We learned that love and hugs and working to understand each other can make a huge difference in a journey like ours. We learned that Parkinson's disease was the enemy and we weren't going to let it get away with stealing our quality of life.

Annie showed remarkable resilience and continuously taught me what was working and not working. We learned together, step after step through our journey. We proved that despite the fact her condition was worsening, we could go from having three major falls with significant injuries in one year to two relatively minor falls over the next ten years. Those two falls likely occurred as a result of fainting episodes due to autonomic-induced low blood pressure, which is relatively common in late-stage Parkinson's disease.

We had two things working against us: the ever-present disease and the fact we were getting older. It is easy to blame all of our challenges on the disease – and indeed, it was the major problem – but we were getting older, too. It is certainly easier to age if you don't have a neurodegenerative disease.

We held a small, private funeral because of the COVID concerns at that time. The pandemic situation had improved by that summer and the snowbirds were back in Wisconsin, so in August we held a celebration of life event at Oneida Country Club. About 250 people showed up despite the rain, and the parking lot was so full that some people didn't even come in. It was a good day for our family, and we heard many nice comments from those in attendance. We had adapted to Annie's physical loss and were able to celebrate her.

I love Annie and I don't want to let go of her spiritual presence. I wake up and look at her picture every morning and say, "Good morning, Annie. I love you. Let us pray." It is a continuation of our routine from when she was still alive. I say that twice a day; three times if I make a visit to the cemetery. We would pray the Lord's Prayer, sometimes followed by the prayer we used when she would have a bad day and we weren't able to turn things around right away:

"God, you have so eminently blessed Annie and me. You have given us life on this wonderful earth. You have given us wonderful parents, family, and friends. Most of all, you have given us each other. You brought us together in that research lab at UW-Madison in the summer of 1963. You continued to bless us because you've given us many wonderful years filled with blessings such as three remarkable children, and through them eight special grandchildren, and so many other relatives, friends, and people who are important in our lives."

I was somewhat oblivious to the physical impact that Parkinson's disease was having on Annie's appearance over the years. I was astounded looking at photos after she passed, some of which you see in this book. The disease robbed her of the physical vitality that had been her calling card. To me, she was always beautiful.

My perception of how well I was doing emotionally was totally dependent on keeping Annie happy. I never regretted one second of time not being able to do something else because of caring for Annie. It was indeed a labor of love, although I did not consider it to have been labor at all. We bonded more closely as time went on. She didn't always say thank you, but she didn't need to.

Did our efforts make a difference in the quality of our lives together? You bet they did.

Chapter 10

The Brain Center
of Green Bay

In 2015, about six years prior to Annie's passing, I literally ran into a retired psychiatrist friend of mine named Dr. Dave Donarski. I had just dropped off Annie at the dentist and was filling the time with an easy run on Webster Avenue. Dave, who was a classmate of my brother's at Marquette University Medical School, was out for a walk when we crossed paths. I paused my run for a brief chat, and we talked a little about running and walking before Dave changed the subject.

"How's Ann?" he asked.

"We're challenged, but doing okay," I answered.

"You and I should sit down and talk sometime about what can be done for people like her," Dave said.

"That's a damn good idea," I replied before continuing on my way.

Dave and I started to meet every Tuesday at eight o'clock in the morning at our kitchen table. I had cut back dramatically on my work-load by this time as I transitioned into full-time retirement, and Annie usually was in bed during Dave's visits. We would have a cup of coffee and talk about things for an hour or so.

A few months later, in January of 2016, is when I came across that *Wall Street Journal* article about Dr. Norman Doidge's book, *The Brain's Way of Healing*. The article talked about neuroplasticity and the ability of the brain to change itself. It delivered a "Wow!" moment for me. I picked up a copy of Doidge's book immediately and devoured it in one day. There were two chapters in the book covering Parkinson's disease, and he described the PoNS tongue stimulation device being developed at UW-Madison.

"Dave, you've got to see this book!" I told him.

The information in Doidge's book really motivated us. Not long af-terward, I ran into family medicine specialist Daniel Koster, MD, and his wife Michelle, a fellowship-trained orthodontist. Michelle's grand-mother was the house mother at a sorority house in Madison. In a small-world moment, Annie had worked at that sorority house while she was a student to make money by serving meals and helping in the kitchen. This was a year before we met in the lab.

Dan and Michelle Koster started joining Dave Donarski and me on Tuesday mornings, along with retired orthopedic surgeon Richard Horak, MD. We didn't know at the time, but these meetings eventually would lead to the formation of the Brain Center of Green Bay, Inc.

I showed the group Doidge's book, and everyone was very excited about the information it offered. We decided we really wanted to tour the PoNS lab in Madison, but that was easier said than done. We had difficulty reaching the individuals involved in that program. Thankful-ly, I had connections through the University of Wisconsin Foundation, and several of us went down for a tour of the Waisman Center research facilities and the TCNL (Tactile Communication and Neurorehabilita-tion Laboratory). The lab opened in 1992 and closed at the end of 2017, meaning we made our visit just in time.

The TCNL had run into roadblocks at the FDA level, which is why Annie and I had to travel to Canada to try out the PoNS device. The de-vice is now available in the USA for individuals with multiple sclerosis (MS) and has been used with people experiencing residual symptoms following head injuries.

Gradually, our group began sharing ideas more actively about what a non-profit organization focused on brain health could look like. I also mentioned the concept to Jon Pahl, a Lutheran minister who later would serve on our board of directors. Jon had started two non-profits when he lived in Philadelphia and had a great deal of expertise in getting such an organization started.

"Do you have a developmental plan yet?" he asked me.

"No, that's next on our list," I replied.

"I'd love to help you out," Jon said.

Two weeks later, we had our developmental plan. The Brain Center of Green Bay, Inc., incorporated in December of 2017. The Greater Green Bay Community Foundation allowed us to operate under its umbrella. This made it easy for donations to flow through that foundation and then to the Brain Center. All five of the Brain Center's founding individuals served on the initial board of directors, and we added Vince Schamber, CPA, as our treasurer.

It took us a year to really get going. We needed to build our board of directors and raise some capital to cover our legal bills and other expenses. The next person to join the board of directors was Deb Mauthe, the former human resources director at Prevea Clinic in Green Bay. I knew Deb well from my position on the Prevea board. Her daughter, Kelsey O'Donnell-Mauthe, later would become our office manager.

We built our board to more than a dozen people, and more importantly, a couple of significant benefactors became involved. We rented space in a church basement for serving our clients and holding Brain Center business meetings, and officially opened on January 1, 2020.

We were just getting going when the COVID pandemic hit in March, forcing us to shut down along with the rest of the world. The coaching we had been doing with individuals and families going through neurodegenerative journeys shifted to virtual meetings. Fundraising was coming along well enough that once COVID was over, the stage was set to move forward.

At first, the Brain Center staff included just Dave Donarski and me, and then we added volunteers, a registered nurse, and a social worker. But what to do next? Should we find work for our volunteer coaches group? Hire an executive director? Hire an office manager?

We hired Kelsey as our office manager first, and then it was time to look for an executive director. Deb Mauthe recommended Christine Vanden Hoogen, an experienced fundraiser with local and regional ties. Bringing her onboard was a slam-dunk decision for us. She knows how to approach the various foundations and get people involved in the mission of a non-profit like ours.

The Brain Center relocated to the Cerebral Palsy, Inc., building, just minutes from my home. CP had space available and its board likes what we're doing. We have great interactions with the CP staff and their clients, even extending to school children who tour the building.

Our goal for the Brain Center is not to duplicate programs that other organizations offer. We don't want to take programs away from organizations that already are doing them well. We also want to serve as a resource for other organizations.

We resolved that the Brain Center would not take the place of our clients' doctors. What we can do is tell people what we have learned and hopefully help them make their journey as smooth as possible. I know from first-hand experience that support from care partners can positively impact the future course of the disease. You can slow it down. Remember, the enemy is the disease, not the care person or their care partner.

We coach and educate people on the tools they need to live safe and fulfilling lives. So much of what we're doing with the Brain Center has its origins in what I did with Annie. I learned under fire while caring for her. We try to impress upon care partners the need to understand the fine line between providing appropriate care and being overprotective. They have to understand their care partner has to feel as though they retain some control over their lives or they are going to rebel. This is a critical distinction.

"My family won't let me do anything," one woman told me. "They won't allow me to do the things I can still do."

Of course, it is important for us to hear both sides of the story because of the dementia aspect common with many of these diseases. All care decisions are safety first, but allowing your care partner to have some control goes a long way toward their ongoing cooperation.

People often leave the Brain Center saying, "I've got a future. I can still have a life."

Part of our role there is to meet with people – usually couples – who are struggling with the physical and emotional challenges of living with neurodegenerative disease. Sometimes they are early in their journeys, but more commonly they at a point farther along. The sessions are either in person or via Zoom, and can take two hours or more. I begin by asking them to tell me their story. They are often afraid, stressed, worried, and frustrated. They want to know what's going on. There can be no secrets. I often share Annie's stories during coaching sessions because they are so impactful.

I find that coaching energizes me. I spend a lot of time explaining the key points of what they have to live with, and that both of them have to take responsibility for making good decisions. If the Parkinson's patient is not able to do so, then the spouse must. Having children or other family members who can contribute to this effort is very important. It takes a team, especially when the care partner begins having their own issues. Aging is not for sissies, whether you have a disorder such as Parkinson's disease or not.

I had a Zoom conversation with a couple in which the husband, not yet sixty years old, was in the intermediate stages of Parkinson's. His wife was off camera, but he let me know she was there. Not long after we began the session, I could sense a little background about our journey may be helpful.

"I have to tell you about my wife," I began. "We were flying high in life and then bingo – she lost her sense of smell."

I saw the man's face change. He had a neutral expression, and then the tears came. His wife moved over to comfort him.

"You don't have to worry about having tears," I said. "I cry all the time. It helps me deal with all the wonderful memories I have. They are tears of love. We will be talking about personal things today, and it is okay to cry."

"You have to know," his wife said, "I love him and I understand this is not his fault. But I can't do it 24/7. I may have to have somebody else help."

"None of us can do it alone," I reassured her. "We find ways. For example, I got so much accomplished when Annie was sleeping. People with Parkinson's disease need that additional rest, but then you include them in everything else."

A coach can only open their client's eyes to what they can do, what they can control. For example, it is virtually impossible to comprehend what it's like to deal with autonomic nerve dysfunction until you experience it with your care person. You have the strength of your relationship on your side, and that is huge. Don't underestimate the power of love.

A high level of awareness has developed on issues involving care for the care partner as it relates to the national focus on mental health. It is so critical for family members and friends to provide emotional support for care partners. You will burn out as a care partner if you don't have a support system. This is something I emphasize during coaching sessions.

Ideally, a loving spouse is able to serve as the primary care partner. That does not necessarily mean everybody is suited for this role. Some couples can't get along or are short-sighted in accepting how their situation likely will play out. You have a choice to cooperate with each other or not.

We were blessed. I learned I was a lucky man who had a wonderful wife. That made the difference. We were each other's best friends and lovers. We were committed to each other. I was her care partner and she was mine. I have no doubt about that.

***

Annie's legacy can be beneficial to so many people going forward. I hope we are able to build bridges between the Brain Center of Green Bay, the Boston University CTE Center, and Parkinson's-focused organizations such as the Davis Phinney Foundation, the Michael J. Fox Foundation, the Wisconsin Parkinson's Association, and others. Ours is an ongoing journey that has not ended.

The Brain Center proves there is more to life than our day-to-day existence. I talk about this openly with people I meet during coaching sessions, but I do it in a matter-of-fact way. I don't have any secrets with people I meet at the Brain Center or our friends.

We don't necessarily have control about how or when we lose our physical life. I can tell you Annie's spiritual soul is within me, and that is so comforting. I need that feeling because it keeps me going, and I don't need to understand it fully. Spirituality is so important in this journey.

Was her Parkinson's tough for me to accept at first? Yes, our life changed. It is tough for me to accept it even now. I miss hugging her. That's why I look at her picture many times every day.

You were a huge eye-opener for me and many other people, Annie. Thanks to the Brain Center of Green Bay, your story continues to grow. It is more than just your legacy.

As of this writing in 2023, we have five very active volunteer coaches, including three retired physicians, a retired RN, two active experienced social workers, and two other experienced healthcare workers who provide immense help in our programming. Our objective is to share information, coaching, and support on a local level as research continues on a global scale.

For example, the Michael J. Fox Foundation announced some exciting news as we were in the final stages of writing this book with the discovery of a Parkinson's biomarker. According to the foundation, this highly accurate biological test is capable of objectively and reliably detecting the disease at the molecular level, even before the onset of symptoms. This is the first biomarker capable of identifying people with Parkinson's or at risk for Parkinson's through abnormal alpha-synuclein, which is the protein that twists abnormally in the Parkinson's brain.

Would early testing have helped Annie? It's impossible to say. It's easier to connect the dots looking in the rearview mirror than it is in the moment. Yes, a test like this would have given us a head start on preparing for challenges that might come up.

Victories can be little or big, and we need to celebrate all of them. Establishing the Brain Center of Green Bay, Inc., is a big victory that I hope will generate all types of victories long after I am gone.

You can learn more about the Brain Center of Green Bay on our website, https://www.braincentergb.org/. You also can contact the center by phone at 920-393-4080 or email info@braincentergb.org.

Chapter 11

Final Thoughts

The journey that Annie and I took together generated loads of learning that I now enjoy sharing with others. We learned some things the hard way, and it is my hope that this book encourages you to learn how to make a difference early on in your life as well as that of your loved ones. Let's cover a few topics here that can make your journey a little easier:

***

I say a prayer every morning to get my day going. There are benefits in waking up your body to wake up your brain to wake up your spiritual soul. If you don't think so, just wait until something happens.

When Annie lost her ability to know what she was doing, I had to know for her. Parkinson's, and aging itself, causes a general apathy and unawareness of what is going on around you. I see this occurring with my own decision making, and I am aware I have to be careful about it.

For example, I did a half-marathon in the spring of 2023 without major difficulties. I was on a high when I got to the finish line. I won the 80-85 age group, my family was proud of me, and I was proud of me. My left Achilles' tendon bothered me when I walked, but for some reason it didn't cause discomfort when I ran that day. I rested it for three weeks after that race and figured I would have no problem running our local Bellin Run 10K race in mid-June, since it is less than half the distance of a 13.1-mile half-marathon.

My stubborn brain said I could do it even though my body was telling me otherwise. Well, I got to about the halfway mark and all of a sudden my Achilles said it had enough. I tried to run and couldn't. I tried to walk and hobbled. I looked like the old fart that I am. It took me an hour and ten minutes just to do the last three miles.

This is an example of how we need to know ourselves and make sound judgements in the present, not the brain or body you had in the past. It gets harder to do as we get older, so you can imagine how difficult that is for somebody with a Parkinson's brain. Annie could still make good decisions early in her journey. She had the awareness in the 1980s to realize she couldn't play tennis anymore and switched to coaching.

That ability slowly, but steadily declined as her condition progressed, leaving me and other family members to assume more responsibility. Unreasonable denial will become part of the dementia portion of your care person's journey. You must prepare yourself to be strong and make tough decisions when faced with your own situations.

***

It can be easy to become overwhelmed with the science involved when it comes to Parkinson's and other neurodegenerative diseases. My advice is to take on as much as you can handle, but don't lose sleep over it if that topic is not your interest. Your job is to focus on safety and quality of life. Understanding how the brain works in simple terms might give you some level of comfort when you see changes occurring in your or your care person's behavior, motions, or attitude.

Think of the brain as a factory with jobs to do. It needs energy to turn on the lights so it can produce a product. Brain cells act like employees, and every cell needs energy to perform at peak efficiency. The products that brain cells produce include memories, logical thought, interpreting what's going on around you, and controlling critical systems. It is a complex operation, just like a factory. Lewy bodies destroy brain cells, which essentially is like laying off factory employees or taking equipment offline permanently.

For the most part, we can't make new brain cells, but we can form new pathways in areas of the brain that are not affected by those destructive Lewy bodies. This is where neuroplasticity comes into play. We can retrain the brain to take a different route to the same outcome. Although a smoldering fire may destroy part of a factory, we can relocate some functions to other parts of the building.

When a factory's production line has a problem, quality experts look for the root cause. The same goes for doctors and other healthcare professionals when it comes to our bodies and brains. Parkinson's is like a smoldering fire in the brain. Every so often, it flares up and Parkinson's gets worse. Maybe it's a urinary tract infection that fuels the fire. Sometimes the best corrective action is shutting down the production line. For Annie, it was making her laugh, hugging her, and engaging her in something positive. I learned not to criticize her; that only fanned the flames of that smoldering Parkinson's fire.

We know we can't get rid of that smoldering fire, but we can minimize or delay the flare-ups. At the end of her life, those smoldering flames took away Annie's awareness of what was going on. The flames quietly extinguished her physical body and allowed her to sleep away peacefully.

***

I mentioned several times that I have two major regrets when it comes to Annie's journey. One is that we hugged a lot, but still should have hugged more. The other is that we didn't know what would develop into problems until it was too late.

Chewing and swallowing are on the top of my list for that second regret. By the time I realized that her weight was an issue, it had become part of that smoldering fire of Parkinson's. Her brain was starving and I didn't pay attention to it at first. You don't notice it when your care person loses a pound or two per year, but before you know it, they've lost fifteen pounds in six years. Annie didn't have fifteen pounds to lose.

You have to get calories in at all costs. Protein is good, but healthy fats need to be part of the diet as well. Get coconut oil and add it to a smoothie if you have to. Everything in our body is a balancing act. We need just enough, not too much or too little. A disease process like Parkinson's makes that balancing act much more difficult to sustain.

***

I come back to my favorite 'L words' in reinforcing some of the most important aspects of being an effective care partner: Listen, Look, Learn, Like, Lead, Laugh, Love, Light, and Legacy. Annie's legacy is the Brain Center of Green Bay and the way she lived. It is exciting because we're able to do more for people who are on their own journeys.

Make today a good day and don't wait until tomorrow. We always had something to look forward to, whether it was a trip to Florida, spending time with friends, or attending a wedding. We went to every wedding we could, and each one energized us with a dose of happiness.

Our friends groups played an important role throughout our adult lives. Our military group, our University of Wisconsin alumni group, our Green Bay medical group, our tennis group, and others all kept us engaged in living life. We also enjoyed what I call "circumfriendtial" connections. In other words, we met new friends as a result of interacting with existing friends or just continuing to be an active part of society.

Leverage each of these L words to enjoy your highest quality of life. You won't regret it.

Epilogue

I woke up about three o'clock in the morning on February 12, 2023, as we were nearing the end of the process of putting together this book. I had enjoyed a good five hours of uninterrupted sleep, and I began to think about the deep personal significance of the day's date. It was the second anniversary of Annie's passing.

For some reason, I don't recall thinking of "Annie." Rather, I thought of "Ann" that morning. I thought of her peaceful, progressive, sleeping away from this life without pain, without suffering. She was in our own home; indeed, in our own bedroom and our own bed. We had proudly shared the same bedroom and same bed almost every night of our married lives, beginning on our wedding night of July 18, 1964. Only rarely would business travel, military duties, or other such commitments separate us.

Finally, I told myself to get out of bed and write down some of the

Annie was not a big fan of roughing it, but she was a trooper when we camped in Colorado in 1995, five years after her diagnosis with Parkinson's disease.

thoughts flooding into my consciousness before they disappeared in the distractions of the day. I cried as I quickly jotted notes on a yellow pad, and I find myself near tears as I recall them now. It was a very therapeutic experience.

I had come to the realization that I have been preparing for the intense discovery of the reality of loss. The loss for Annie and for me. She had always been with me, but no longer. We had spent more than fifty-six years sleeping together, living together, snuggling together, talking together, deciding together, making and having babies together, raising children together, hugging together, traveling together, crying together, laughing together, planning together, praying together, just being together.

Overcoming together.

In addition to the reality of loss, I can take comfort in the reality of joy, of discovery, of winning, of losing, of dreams, of nightmares, of life, of death, of our small world, of the huge universe.

I continue to discover who Annie was, who she is, and who she will be. Her passing, I now understand, was just a physical loss. As we grew together, we gained each other. We were no longer separate. We were growing together, we were learning, we were loving, and we were changing.

I became aware of how I was growing, learning, loving, blossoming, and changing as an individual as well. Annie had been doing those things, and all of a sudden I realized, "So am I."

Annie and I were always moving forward in numerous ways together, whether we knew it or not. All of these processes are interconnected. Sometimes they are automatic. Sometimes the process is almost surreal. The fact these connections continue to exist is what makes this so profound. It is why I kept writing. I wasn't trying to find the right words; the right words just came to me.

But why was this happening to me now?

In the last few weeks of Annie's life, the steady spread of Lewy bodies and tau protein clumps was causing her brain to fail. More importantly, I believe that God was ensuring that she was sleeping away peacefully in a deep sleep, without pain or suffering. Andy's wife, Elizabeth, who is a registered nurse, and our caregiver, Sally Ann, would bathe Annie and make sure there were no bed sores.

I would sleep with her and say "I love you" quietly. I did not want to disturb her because I did not want to extend what was going to happen.

On Monday morning, February 8, 2021, four days before she took her last breath, I snuggled up to her. I was barely able to awaken her. I told her I loved her, and she seemed to understand me.

"Would you like a drink of water?" I asked.

"No," she whispered almost imperceptibly.

That was the last word I remember her saying. She was peacefully entering a very deep sleep, essentially comatose. It was her way of telling me she was ready. It was time.

At 4 p.m. the following Friday, February 12, 2021, Annie took her last breath. Sarah and I were with her. Was I prepared for that? Not really, even though I knew it was coming. I don't know if one can ever really be prepared for losing a wonderful wife, best friend, confidante, lover, mother, grandmother, and friend to so many. Intense, shared love and understanding filled our fifty-six and a half years of marriage. We didn't allow the forty-five years of Annie's Parkinson's disease to interfere with that.

But Annie's story didn't end there. In fact, it hasn't ended yet.

Two days after her passing, at 8 a.m. on Sunday morning – which happened to be Valentine's Day – I was sitting at the kitchen table by myself, sipping coffee and reading the newspaper, when without warning, I abruptly bolted out of my chair into a standing position. I had no cognitive awareness to plan doing that. I was reading intently and not even thinking about Annie in that moment.

I tried to figure out what caused me to jump to my feet like that. I surmised it may have been related to the hundreds of similar actions I had taken over the past couple of years when I would think, "I'd better go back to the bedroom and check on Annie."

Sometimes I would hear her call to me, "Rolf?"

"Annie, I'll be right back," I'd respond, and immediately head to the bedroom.

This time, I somewhat jokingly said aloud, "Annie, I'll be right back to check on you."

Then I went back to drinking my coffee and reading my newspaper.

About ten minutes later, I bolted out of my chair again, only this time my reaction included an intense emotional, physical, cognitive eruption of energy. It was three or four times more powerful than what had occurred the first time. My body and brain were instantly aware of the overwhelming spiritual presence of Annie.

I was crying by this time, and shouted out loud, "Annie! You have come back to me! Your spiritual soul has returned to me!"

I rapidly walked back to our bedroom, fully understanding that Annie would not be there. But she was there, because she was within me. I was still crying, and Annie's spiritual presence led me to say loudly, "Thank you, God. You have brought Annie's and my spiritual souls back together again."

Annie was there, God was there, and I was a participant. That hasn't changed.

She and I became one in so many ways during our shared life journey, and I believe my role now is that of being a messenger. Our journey was challenging, but also spiritual. That has become more and more apparent to me.

Annie, you are driving me forward to make a difference. You made a difference when you were here physically, and now you are making a difference spiritually. That is most comforting.

Her resilience and strong will continue to provide the energy that powers my dedication to telling her story, as well as my commitment to helping those in need.

It is Annie's lasting legacy.

Acknowledgements

Producing this book was a journey of its own and served as an energizing next chapter to Annie's legacy and our story. There are a number of people and organizations who have been instrumental in our lives and deserving of thanks, either for their emotional support through our journey or motivating me to move forward with this book. Relationships kept us going through the tough times and continue to engage me today.

As with any list of this type, I realize I run the risk of inadvertently omitting people who were very important to Annie and me. To anyone I do not mention by name, please know that we appreciate the impact you have had on our lives and treasure your friendship. We love you all, and wish you good health and happiness as you continue on your own life's journey.

First, thank you to the many people who urged, "Rolf, you have to write a book about your and Annie's story." This likely is not something I would have undertaken without significant prodding from multiple people, some local and some at a national level.

Thank you to our immediate family members who played important roles throughout our journey regardless of whether they live near or far. Our daughter, Susan Stanley, her husband Monty, and their sons Connor and Carter; our daughter, Sarah, and her daughters Greta, Ingrid, and Claudia; our son, Andy, and his wife Elizabeth, and his children Heidi, Zita, and Wally; my brother, Kim, his wife, Jeannie, and their combined eight children; Annie's sister Kathryn "Sis," her husband Neal Tornblom, and their three children; and our dear family Irish friends James, Willy, and Teresa Fahy.

While they are not blood relatives, Sally Ann Schuyler and Libby Miller became like family as a result of the many hours of in-home care and physical therapy they provided for Annie. Thank you so much for all your efforts in making Annie's life better and providing me with much-needed care assistance.

Thank you to our close friends here in Green Bay, many of whom we have enjoyed wonderful relationships going as far back as our arrival in 1974. These people were with us throughout our journey, traveling with us, celebrating events with us, and generally being awesome human beings. They include Sharon and George Hartmann, Heidi and Jim Mattson, Claire and Chuck McCarthy, Judy and Leo Scherer, Florence and Pat (deceased) Garland, as well as Florence's second husband, Frank Weinhold, Jean and Tom Badciong, Sue and Fred Hollenbeck, Georgia and Jim Kneeland, Shirley Foeller and Jack Williamson, Jean and John Marnocha, and Bonnie and Eliot Elfner. The Elfners were married the exact same day and year as us, and we celebrated our anniversaries together on multiple occasions.

Ann and I shared very respectful friendships with two families that similarly dealt with loved ones who bravely battled degenerative brain diseases. Thank you to the Don Schneider family and the Jim Kress family for your friendships and support.

My medical partners at the old West Side Clinic and now Prevea Clinic provided a very important support network and are close friends. Thank you to Pat and Jim Hinckley, Laura and Mike O'Reilly, Julie and Chris Van Saders, Lauri and Joe Cullen, Patty McDougal Schick and Mark Schick, Bonnie and Bob Kaftan, Steve Bollom, and Ashok Rai.

The list of nurses I have worked with in hospital operating rooms, recovery rooms, patient floors, and at clinic offices is huge. However, I would especially like to recognize Mary Osterloh-Kollman, Carol Willems, Laura O'Reilly, and Pat Yagodinski for their professionalism and friendship.

Annie and I treasured our relationships with several groups of long-standing friends across the country. In addition to those listed below, thank you to all our wonderful friends who included Annie and me in far more than fifty wedding celebrations over the years. Attending weddings was such a positive experience for us and we enjoyed every one of them.

Our University of Wisconsin-Madison alumni group has been with us for more than sixty years. They include Bonnie and Barry Behnken, Sharon and Bill Norton, Diane and Jim Blotz, Rita and Neil "Fred" Wienke, Grace and Jim Flora, Kate (Robinson) and Dick Zimmerman, Carol Bongers and Jim Weiss, Becky Anderson, and Marilyn and Dave Olds.

Annie's close college and La Crosse, Wisconsin, friends include Norrita and Jerry Thorne, Charlene "Shindy" McLaughlin, and Mary and Tom Schilling, Francie and Bob Onley, and Penny and Don Oines. Our Fort Dix friends include Cathy and Dick Diehl, Giesla and Ron Geiger, Frances and Edward "Tony" Rankin, and Gina and Larry Schrock.

I have extreme gratitude for the compassionate interactions and exemplary services provided by the team at the Boston University CTE Center (Boston Brain Bank). Thank you to the lead scientific team of Ann McKee, Bertrand "Russ" Huber, and Thor Stein, and my contact at the Concussion Legacy Foundation, Lisa McHale, Director of Legacy Family Relations. You made the emotionally delicate process of donating Annie's brain one that I am very happy to have pursued.

Thor wanted to hear more about Annie's story while we had dinner together at the 2022 Legacy Family Huddle in Las Vegas. This was a meeting of forty-four families of brain donors who wanted to learn more about the Brain Bank's research. It took place not long after I received their report on Annie. Thor was one of many people to tell me after Annie's passing, "Rolf, you have to write the book."

Thank you to all my colleagues, staff, and board members at the Brain Center of Green Bay for contributing your talents and continuing Annie's legacy. They include Mary and Dave Donarski, Ellen and Dick Horak, Michelle and Dan Koster, Christine Vanden Hoogen, Kelsey O'Donnell-Mauthe, LaReina Tipping, Deb Mauthe, Carolyn and Kramer Rock, Meg Kress Grunwald, Vince Schamber, Byron Conway, Sheri Fairman, and Phil Clampitt.

Kelsey O'Donnell-Mauthe, our office manager, and Kathy Hilgenberg, one of our volunteer coaches and a retired RN, were among the first to strongly suggest I write this book. Kathy had served as the primary care partner for her mother, who had Alzheimer's disease.

Our neighbors on Betty Court showered Annie and me with the type of support and goodwill one would expect in a small-town Midwestern community like Green Bay. Still, know that we never took having good neighbors for granted. You are a major reason Betty Court will always be home. Some of these great neighbors are Julie and Rob Lennon, Becki and Dick Starry, and Sally and John Straub.

Thank you to our clergy connections, Chuck and Jeannie Mize, and Bridget Flad Daniels at Union Congregational Church, and Fr. Paul DeMuth and Bishop Robert Morneau of the Catholic Diocese of Green Bay. Also, my thanks to Jon Pahl, PhD, a former board member at the Brain Center of Green Bay and a part-time minister at Union Congregational

Finally, this book would not be in front of you without the talents and dedication of the husband-wife team of Mike Dauplaise and Bonnie Groessl at M&B Global Solutions Inc. here in Green Bay, Wisconsin. I have had positive relationships with both of them going back several decades.

Bonnie was a department head at St. Mary's Hospital Medical Center and later became a nurse practitioner at Prevea Clinic in Green Bay, two organizations with which I was involved as a physician. She is an author and entrepreneur coach, and helped me organize my thoughts at the outset of the writing process into the primary topics we needed to cover.

I have known Mike and his family for close to fifty years, going back to our earliest days in Green Bay when Mike's father was involved in the running community and his mother was a nurse. Mike has worked as a newspaper reporter, corporate communications specialist, author, editor, and freelance writer for more than forty years. He served as my writing partner and page designer for this project, and met with me weekly for about a year to talk through all the stories and compile information. He did a wonderful job taking my thoughts and crafting them into the final product you see here.

Annie's Eulogy

Written and delivered by our daughter, Sarah Lulloff

Estee was her fragrance.
Olga was her lingerie.
Tennis was her game.
And Rolfie was her flame.

I would have loved to have seen and known my mom when she was younger. She didn't tell many stories, but she had a strong set of principles and sense of self that must have developed in her early years.

The mom I always knew was organized—her life had little clutter. She would often assign my dad the weekend of task of "tackling the piles" of paperwork he created that lined the back hall stairway. We kids often wondered what my mom did all day. In fact, she was so skilled at running the show at home that we never realized all she did. The laundry was always done. Dinner was always on the table ... even if it was orange roughy for the third night that week! It wasn't until we kids were managing our own households that we could acknowledge how effortless she made it look.

The mom I always knew loved to dress up. She called it "getting gussied up." She so looked forward to a party or event and would plan her whole outfit—the dress, the shoes, the earrings, necklace, bracelet, and rings ... right down to the handbag. But even for everyday life, she made it a point to look nice to greet my dad when he got home from work. In her later years, she would send my dad or Sally Ann on a wild goose chase between closets and dressers and jewelry boxes to find the exact pants, sweater, and earrings she had in mind. The search could go on

Ready for tennis in about 1980.

for days, as there were so many potential hiding places. Poor Sally Ann failed to find a piece of clothing that in fact was nestled in the closet in Sanibel. For my mom's seventieth birthday, we had a blast putting on a fashion show of her iconic outfits from each decade—polyester hot pants from the late 1960s onward.

Susan tells how when her date for a ninth-grade dance came to the house to take pictures, she insisted that my mom change out of the plaid pants she was wearing, as they were an embarrassment. Annie L did not give in. Rather, she told the boy's mom of Susan's request, leaving Susan mortified.

The mom I knew struck a remarkable balance of investing in friendships, while prioritizing her family. She could talk for hours on the phone to friends that lived only blocks away. She had countless "tennis friends" and played year-round with a wide range of players, winning city-wide and club championships in both singles and doubles. Her trim figure in a Fila tennis ensemble was enviable! While she loved to get out on the court with my dad, my brother and me, she was equally excited to help foster Susan's interest in horses. She left the horse stall mucking to Susan and Dad, but she made sure Susan's horse had carrots to enjoy. Traveling to horse shows and tennis tournaments for her children gave my mom even more opportunities to socialize and form friendships.

As an adult, I came to appreciate my mom's ability to connect with so many different types of people from different walks of life and with different interests. She could always find something in common to discuss or laugh about. Her charm, her authenticity, her lack of pretenses, and her love of having fun made her good company. Even in recent years, her smile and the sparkle in her eyes gave others joy.

Once, my mom and I drove with my close tennis pal, Amy Malik, and her mom, Jeannie, from their house in Milwaukee out of state for a tennis tournament. Amy recalls how when Rolfie dropped us off at their house, she witnessed something shocking. My mom and dad shared a long kiss in their driveway as they said their good-byes. I thought their affection was what every couple did. I had no idea how special their love for each other was, and how tight their bond always was and will continue to be.

Finally, let's not forget the feisty version of Annie L.

When my dad was hospitalized two years ago for several days, we kids scrambled, with the help of Sally Ann, to keep my mom's routine as "normal" as it could be. One evening, Andrew and Susan and I brought my mom back to their house after visiting my dad at the hospital. She had barely eaten anything that day, so we quickly whipped up a good meal. I placed the salmon, sweet potatoes, and carrots on a plate and set it in front of her. She said, "I'm not hungry." We told her, "You need to eat something—the last you ate was a couple bites of a PB&J five hours ago." She replied, "I already ate a salmon dinner." Susan then offered, "How would you like a brownie?" She countered without skipping a beat, "How would YOU like some dog poop?" Apparently she wasn't hungry.

One of my most recent warming moments with my mom was a couple of weeks before she passed away. The presidential inauguration had already taken place. I spent a Sunday afternoon at Betty Court and sent my dad down to the treadmill for some much-deserved exercise and

"Rolf time." My mom was lying on the sofa, eyes closed, but awake. We chatted a bit. I tried to update her on what was going on in my world and share some uplifting news and stories with her.

Then I recalled the beautiful poem composed and presented by Amanda Gorman on the steps of the US capitol for the new president. I brought it up on the laptop, asked her if she would like to see and hear it. She said yes. For the next several minutes, her eyes remained open and we watched the amazing poem reading together. At the end, I said, "Wasn't that beautiful?" and she responded, "Yes. You could tell it came from the heart." It felt so good to connect with her in that way and see her eyes sparkle.